D1449346

To the Supreme Absolute,

to the lineage of great masters,

to all my teachers,

and to all the writers

whose works I have read

…by the same author

Mend the Mind, Mind the Body, Meet the Soul

Secrets Of Reality

Bridging the gap between
ancient wisdom and
contemporary science

RAJ KAPOOR, MD

CFW
BOOKS

To the beloved memory of my parents,
Jiten and Jai Narain.

Secrets of Reality: Bridging the gap between ancient wisdom
and contemporary science. Copyright © 2006 by Raj Kapoor, MD

ISBN 0-9776858-0-2 (Hard Cover)
ISBN 978-0-9776858-0-6

Library of Congress Control Number: 2005910598

First CFW Books Edition, January 2006

Published by
CFW Books
9102 Babcock Blvd., Suite 101,
Pittsburgh, Pennsylvania, 15237.
412-367-9355.
www.cfwbooks.com

Author Image: *Adrienne DeRosa*
Cover design: Copyright © 2006 by *Raj Kapoor, MD*

Printed in the United States of America

Recognition

I would like to express my gratitude to my wife Nirja, my son Sameer, my daughter Monica, and my sister Manju for their unconditional love and understanding throughout the course of writing this book. Their love is appreciated more than I ever expressed.

A number of friends have inspired me greatly and I owe a special debt of gratitude to them. Each individual whose life path has become part of mine has contributed in some way to this material; each was my teacher during the time we shared.

So in alphabetical order, they are: Kamlesh and Nishi Aggarwal, Subash and Suman Ahuja, Rajiv Ahuja, Surinder and Veena Aneja, Mohinder and Saroj Bahl, Naveen Bhatt, Farhad and Shahnaaz Cama, Paresh and Neelima Chiniwalla, Ongart Chuensumran, Farhad and Hutoxi Contractor, Lilly Dastur, Mahesh Desai, Praful and Bharati Desai, Shirish and Bharati Desai, Vilas Desai, Rup and Molly Dua, Sukhdev and Elisha Grover, Som and Sadhana Gupta, Ravi and Jayashree Janardhanan, Ved and Alka Kaushik, Siva Kedarnath, Juginder and Sucheta Luthra, Neil Niren, Sunder Rao, Randhir and Ramona Sahni, Datar and Bina Singh, Harbans and Prakash Singh, Krishna Kumar Shah, Shantilal Shah, Brij and Usha Sharma, Mohini Sharma, Rahul Tandon, Adie and Jasmin Tamboli, the Late Hari Tayal, Neera Tayal, Sunil and Nita Wadhwani. Naturally, any remaining errors are my responsibility alone.

Many thanks to Lillian Konesky for transcription, Tish Doll for secretarial support, and Linda D'Antonio for research and library assistance.

The illustrations found in this book are part of my life long labor of love and are a product of many years of thought and creativity. I am deeply indebted to James Derosa III for his indispensable help in translating my original concepts, artwork and book design into the beautiful images seen here.

My heartfelt gratitude to my editor Terry Newman for her editing, which gave life to these pages and helped the manuscript evolve to its present form.

And above all, I give thanks for the opportunity to join together as one, in mind and heart, throughout the time that you are engaged in *Secrets of Reality*. It was you in the eye of my mind as this material coalesced. It is to you that I dedicate all of the love and understanding that may result from this text, for it is you who are ushering in a new wisdom.

Contents

Macrocosm

Fabric of Space-Time

Elegant Universe

Conscious Universe

Secrets

Microcosm

Biocosm

Circle of Life

Blueprint of Life

Secrets

Reality

Self-Aware Universe

Perception

Karmic Footprints

Secrets

References

Index

Preface

This book got started twenty years ago, when in the course of my teaching I kept bumping against ancient wisdom. Not wisdom in the ordinary sense of the term, but wisdom, nonetheless, in the utter violation of the way we think the world works. The wisdom that I came across had to do with hard scientific evidence. These discoveries left me with a sense of wonder but also profoundly unsettled. All this wisdom was based on an entirely different paradigm of the Reality. This compounded into a new view of the world. May it be a powerful positive force in your life and blessing to you.

- Raj Kapoor

Quest for Reality

Let us admit what all idealists admit — the hallucinatory nature of the world. Let us do what no idealist has done — let us search for unrealities that confirm that nature…We (that indivisible divinity that operates in us) have dreamed the world. We have dreamed it as enduring, mysterious, visible, omnipresent in space and stable in time; but we have consented to tenuous and eternal intervals of illogicalness in its architecture that we might know it is false.

-- *Jorge Luis Borges*, Other Inquisitions

The world is an illusion.

The pre-eminent Argentinean essayist Borges made this simple statement. It could very well, though, be a timeless quote from a mystic or an 'idealist.' But an idea proposed by a physicist? It hardly seems to be an appropriate statement for a scientist to make. This is, indeed, the conclusion of many who specialize in quantum physics, the branch of science that investigates the subatomic realm. Up until the twentieth century, the empirical approach – the physics of Newton – stated unequivocally that the world around us existed independently of human consciousness.

Objectivity. That was the hallmark of a true scientist. But now quantum physics tells us we can never be totally objective about Reality. It is inevitable that the human mind intrudes, with all its preconceived notions and prejudices. The physicists explain that the Reality we see, touch, and feel around us is not our objective view of the world. Rather, Reality is a combination of the quantifiable and immutable laws of the physical world and the subjective view point of the observer.

This paradigm shift does more than challenge our most deeply held scientific and religious beliefs. It has the potential to radically change the way we view, and more importantly, how we *affect* Reality in the future. In many ways, our understanding of the world has come full circle. It appears that what the philosophers have said for ages is now being confirmed and quantified by the scientists in all disciplines: We really do influence Reality and hence our destiny.

In Western culture, science and philosophy answer distinctly different – yet both powerfully vital – questions. Researchers immerse themselves in science to answer *how* the world works. Philosophy answers *why* the world is as it is.

Imagine the route of the two disciplines as parallel lines – whose content never meets. Science learns through experimentation and examination. Philosophers answer the larger questions of life through thoughtful contemplation.

That is, until the twentieth century when unexplained phenomenon continued to appear in the answers of both quantum physicists and astrophysicists. Soon even the study of molecular biology posed questions that science alone could not answer.

And with each unanswered question and puzzling paradox, the men of science found that the parallel lines of these studies slowly – almost imperceptibly began to curve towards each other until the disciplines more closely resemble each other. The parallel lines of these two subjects are slowly coming to form a circle as we find that one subject matter provides support for the other. Indeed, science and philosophy have come full circle.

This book is an attempt to reconcile the two disciplines and bend those parallel lines towards a circle of understanding in a Quest for Reality. Many of us find it difficult to understand science. Those who know the most about it insist on speaking in a jargon the rest of us can't fathom. We are left in the dark about the exciting discoveries and their potential impact on our lives. Similarly, philosophers talk in esoteric terms about subject matter that, at first glance, seems to have little meaning to our everyday lives. This book attempts to explain both of these areas in a fashion that is not only understandable and enjoyable, but useful.

Secrets of Reality shatters those assumptions by employing the adage that 'a picture is worth a thousand words.' Viewed in pictorial or graphic form, such technically challenging subjects such as quantum physics and astrophysics as well as molecular biology, gain clarity and crispness. Philosophical questions, similarly, come into greater focus.

I hope you experience a fresh perspective on the progress of bringing these two disciplines into harmony. Long thought to be antagonistic, more and more the experiments and studies in the field of science are only confirming the validity and the truth of ancient philosophical wisdom.

Secrets of Reality is neither about science nor philosophy, but at its fundamental core is about Consciousness or True Reality. True Reality is that which lies beyond the senses, that which cannot be touched or perceived. It cannot be described because it is beyond the realm of words. It can only be reached experientially.

This bold attempt at reconciling the two disciplines naturally divides itself into four separate – yet related – sections. We work and play within the framework of Newtonian physics, where every action has an equal and opposite reaction and every cause has an effect. But our reality is sandwiched between the unnaturally bizarre world of quantum physics, molecular biology, and the great expanse of the universe.

In the subatomic world of quantum physics, the Newtonian Laws fail. A bizarre set of rules replace them – usually too quirky for many us to understand. I've named this section of our investigation 'nanocosm' – derived from the Greek word 'nano'—meaning small and 'cosm' meaning world. Through word and illustration, we'll study how quantum physics is helping to slowly curve the parallel lines of the two disciplines.

Physicists digging into the quantum realm continually discovered 'paradoxes' because they used the speed of light as their anchor – their frame of reference. *Nothing* can travel faster than that. It was the one given they had in their puzzling journey. Yet the apparent paradoxes piled up. Their studies produced more – and often more peculiar – questions. Pure scientific research failed to answer the '*why?*'

Cause and effect – Newton's strict law – is lost at the nanocosm level. Proving that subatomic particles can indeed communicate faster than the speed of light, scientists tried to fit a round peg into a square hole. They were left frustrated and bewildered.

However, when you use consciousness as your frame of reference in understanding the movements of the subatomic wave-particle duality – an entire vista of possibilities opens. What is faster than the speed of light? The speed of thought. Scientists lacked this vital component in their understanding of this subject matter:

Consciousness or True Reality. When you understand – and we'll show you in both word and picture just what we mean – that consciousness is the key ingredient, then quantum physics makes sense. And it creates a relevancy for our everyday lives.

Similarly, science has yet to answer all the questions about the origins and nature of the universe at large. Addressed in the section 'macrocosm' (macro meaning large and cosm meaning world), current theory fails to explain what happened before the Big Bang – before time and space began. The alternative steady-state theory also is incomplete in many ways.

While scientists are getting tantalizingly close to 'seeing God' as they inch closer to a general unified theory, our understanding of such concepts of space-time and eternity and infinity is limited. 'Black holes' in our knowledge still hamper our full understanding.

Again, we can turn to the ancient Vedic Masters who know that everything in nature is cyclical – including the universe itself. Their intriguing revelations – literally thousands of years old – are eerily similar to what the most brilliant minds in astrophysics are slowly concluding.

As we uncover the layers of knowledge, nature is revealing a Reality that the mystics have been privileged to viewing for millennia. The universe – and everything in it, including our physical selves – could very well be a kind of holographic image. As amazing as this sounds, it brings us sitting closer to the ancient precipice of *Maya* – world is an illusion.

We can also look no further than our own microcosm to find the parallel lines of science and philosophy slowly curving toward on another, closing in an infinite circle. It is DNA that gives us our single identity as a species and also provides us with our individuality in a sea of humanity. The union of a sperm and an egg alone do not generate another living human being. It takes, an extra 'something', scientists say, to create a human being. It requires a third element. Could this be the 'karmic impressions' Vedic Masters have long talked about?

It appears that the two parallel lines of learning – philosophy and science are curving uniformly towards the other inevitably and creating a circle. A circle of knowledge in which scientific ideas flow freely from philosophic concepts and back into science again.

Fully understanding the secrets that nature is finally revealing through our scientific inquiry better equips us to lead a life of spiritual fulfillment. That may seem like a paradoxical statement. You'll soon find that nature is filled with apparent paradoxes – until you know the secret keys to unlocking them – it requires seeing the world in a different light.

The History that Vanished

Our Quest for Reality begins four billion years after the creation of the planet, with the first appearance of mankind. Our earliest human ancestor – native to the African grasslands – is nearly five million years old. In that time, our relatives gradually migrated to all parts of the globe, developing many different civilizations.

No two civilizations over the last five million years grew with the same speed, nor in the same direction. Some developed 'technology' quickly, while others of the same era took a route of staying closer to nature. Even today, there exist vast gulfs among societies. Indeed, these marked differences have always been with us.

The earliest of human civilizations grew in the river valleys of Africa and Asia. More than 6,000 years ago the Sumerians built some of the world's first cities between the Tigris and Euphrates rivers in western Asia. Slowly, our ancestors migrated; cities developed along the Niles River in Africa, the Yellow River in China, and in the Indus Valley in the Indian subcontinent.

 While Egypt and Mesopotamia (the civilization between the Tigris and Euphrates) left us written remnants of their culture, the Indus people for the most part did not. All we know of them comes to us from the very brief description of their seals. Unfortunately, no archeologist or linguist has been able to decipher the seals, as there is no counterpart of the Rosetta stone.

We do know the people of the Indus Valley devised a method of counting, as well as weighing and measuring. Unfortunately our knowledge of this civilization is small and must be classified as 'pre-historic' since it pre-dates the written records of the culture.

The two great cities of the northern Indian subcontinent, Harappa and Mohenjodaro, provide us with some striking archeological evidence on the advanced state of the culture. These excavated sites display metropolitan centers, with intense organization and technological advances in 'urban culture.' Wide streets, large city blocks, bathrooms with drains are but a few of the 'surprises' archeologists discovered. The Indus people were far more advanced than thought. Their use of technology foreshadows the triumphs of the Roman Empire. The incredibly sophisticated culture blossomed between 2300 and 2000 B.C.

Eventually, the culture collapsed. This was partially due to a widespread migratory movement of charioteering peoples, which, in fact, changed the entire face of the civilized world at the time. A group calling themselves *Aryas* invaded the Indus Valley. We've anglicized the name to produce the word 'Aryan.' Invasion was not a one-time event, but a series of actions spanning several hundred years and many different tribes.

Groups of *Aryas* first converged on the plains of India from central Asia by way of the mountain passes of Afghanistan around 1500 B.C. Some of these groups also invaded Iran. In fact, Iranian religions of the *Avesta* – the sacred scripture of Zoroastrianism – and that of the *Vedas* of India closely resemble each other on several different topics.

The natives of Indus Valley called the river *Sindhu*. The Persians, who possessed a natural difficulty in pronouncing the letter S, called it the *Hindu*. It wasn't long before the people who lived there were called Hindus as well. Shortly thereafter the word Hindu entered the Greek vocabulary and the '-ism' was added to 'Hindu' to denote both the culture and the way of life. The entire land of the Indus River became known as India.

Among the people who eventually came to call India home in the second millennium B.C. was a group of related tribes. Their priests had perfected a unique poetry – carefully continued through the generations – solely by oral tradition. These priests employed this poetic art form in the hymns of praise for their Gods, which were sung at sacrifices.

The *Vedas*, as they came to be known from the Sanskrit word knowledge, were originally revealed to the ancient sages (*rsi*) while they were in deep meditation. This mystical experience of 'intonation' was a momentous event. The mystics were able to retrieve this pre-existent knowledge from the ether or space. Called *anahata*, or unstruck sound, these vibrations float freely in the ether and can only be heard in a state of higher meditation. They are imperceptible in the physical sense. This is in contrast to audible sounds, which travel through the air and are produced by a physical shock. Audible sounds are called *ahata*, or 'struck.'

For eons, this information was not written down, but rather handed from generation to generation orally and tightly guarded. Unlike the holy scriptures of other cultures, these hymns contained much more than just praises to the Gods. The *Vedas* revealed sacred knowledge about a host of different topics, including mathematics and science.

Not *one* syllable of these verses had been altered during transmission from one *Veda* master to the next. It is difficult for us to even comprehend in our secular society the extreme sanctity these hymns held in their culture. They survive – even today – in a form, which appears not to have changed for nearly 3,000 years. The *Vedas* still stand today as the most sacred of the holy texts of the Hindus and revered as revelation (*sruti*) and the source of Natural Laws.

Eventually Sanskrit developed a written tradition, but even then, these hymns were rarely written down. The elegant period of the *Vedas* and *Upanishads* – the hymns they chanted – proved to be a transition period in Indian culture from prehistory to history.

The *Vedas* are unique in world religions. They have no single historical founder, no centralized authority or bureaucratic structure. *Vedas* contain no unified code of conduct. But the all encompassing impact of the *Vedas* is immeasurable. To this day, even the humblest of Indians recall the names of *Rishis* and Yoga Masters who lived nearly 1,000 before Christ. An orthodox Hindu repeats hymns in his daily worship, which were composed much earlier. China is the only other country that rivals India in having the oldest continuous cultural tradition in the world.

The path of knowledge in the Western world, however, took a different turn. Western civilization followed the ideas of the early Greek philosophers. Our concepts of philosophy, science, astronomy, art and even psychology can be traced back to ancient Greece. That is not to say that originally even the Greek thinkers were not influenced by the Vedic Masters in some way.

It wasn't even until the fifth century B.C. that the early Greeks even realized the wealth of knowledge India held. The Greeks themselves contained an outstanding tradition of learning. But when Pythagoras visited India – as well as Babylonia, Phoenicia and Egypt – he came away dazzled by the advanced state of India. Modern historians cannot help but draw parallels between his teachings following his visit and that of the Vedic Masters. His biographers have called him the Greek *rsi* (Vedic sage) who taught reincarnation, vegetarianism and more.

Sanskrit

Sanskrit language is absolutely phonetic. It is pronounced exactly as written and is written exactly as it is pronounced. Since the Vedic revelation was revealed in this language it has also been called the language of the Gods. It is written in Devanagri script from left to right and is the mother of all Indo-European languages.

In fact, the geometric theorem which bears his name was known to the Vedic Masters long before he began employing and teaching it in Greece. During his travels, it is evident that Pythagoras studied the mysteries of harmonious music. Later, he discovered the geometry and associated mathematical ratios behind western music. He understood that the underlying universe is defined by mathematical ratios, which are musical in nature.

Soon, however, a chasm formed between the study of philosophy and science. This proved especially true by the 17th century in the Western cultures of Europe. The gulf – not discouraged by The Church who guarded their authority over the people jealously – eventually created two distinct roads in the search for knowledge.

Science and philosophy eventually came to be separate studies. Perhaps the period of the Renaissance would be the last age to experience the thrill of merging fine art with engineering as Leonardo Da Vinci did or meshing science with an innate understanding of philosophy.

And while part of the reason is the increasing control of The Church, the other reason is the clarity and reasonableness of Isaac Newton and his mechanical view of the world around us. Newton took the gulf that The Church had been making and with his discovery of his laws of motions and his view of the world as a giant clock, made it even bigger.

It took the appearance of quantum physics in the early twentieth century to begin to close that gap. The reuniting of science and philosophy is not without its controversies, as you are about to see. We – as citizens in a mostly secular society – find ourselves rediscovering the *Upanishads* and the *Vedas* once more.

Many contend that the true philosophers of today are the scientists who are revealing the surprising world of quantum physics in the subatomic sphere, a vast inherent unrecognized reservoir of intelligence within biology, perhaps even providing us with a glimpse of God in the study of astrophysics.

And what does all this mean for us? We finally come to realize – and appreciate – the true grandeur of all that is around us, just as we come to realize our full potential to influence our Reality.

The Nature of Sound

Sound is considered to be of two kinds, one a vibration of ether, the other a vibration of air. The vibration of ether, which cannot be perceived in the physical sense, is considered the principle of all manifestation, the basis of all substance, the 'music of the spheres.' It forms permanent numerical patterns, which are the basis of world's existence. This kind of vibration is not caused by physical shock, as are audible sounds. It is therefore called anahata, 'unstruck.' The other kind of sound is an impermanent vibration of air, an image of ether vibration. It is audible and always produced by a shock. It is therefore called ahata or 'struck.'

'Struck sound is said to give pleasure, unstruck sound leads to liberation.' (Narada Purana)

From Zero to Infinity

0. Zero. As a mathematical concept it is indispensable. As a symbol the zero is immediately identifiable. Its use extends far beyond pure mathematics. Zero is embedded in our culture and is known by many names: zilch, zip, nada, nothing … goose egg … the list goes on.

Yet it may surprise you to learn that the symbol – and the concept it represents – was not always a part of mathematics or ancient cultures.

The Babylonians, the Egyptians, and the Greeks added, subtracted, multiplied, and divided without a zero. The Romans, though, faced a unique challenge. It is impossible to multiply using their bulky numerical system, where four is represented as IV, ten, as X, and fifty, as C. You cannot multiply 1980 by 10 in Roman numerals:

$$MCMLXXX \times X = ? \qquad 1980 \times 10 = 19,800$$

It wasn't until 130 AD that Ptolemy added the letter 'omicron' to act as a zero in the Sumerian number system, which is based on 60. But this was not widely used and eventually fell into disuse.

The use of zero as we know it today began in ancient India. Mathematicians in the seventh century very often would use a word, much like Ptolemy, to indicate the absence of a number. This avoided confusing 65 with 605 or even with 650. Represented originally by a dot, it eventually evolved into the recognizable symbol of zero we use today.

The first archeological evidence of its use is dated 876 AD on an Indian tablet. However, earlier writings found reference to the concept, attesting to the struggles inherent in making the symbol an integral part of the numerical system.

Brahmagupta, a Hindu astronomer and mathematician, attempted 200 years before the first written evidence of this place-holder symbol, to define the operations involving zero. Addition and subtraction certainly posed no problem with its use. And similarly multiplying with a zero was not difficult: any number multiplied by zero is zero.

Performing division posed a set of problems, though. Brahmagupta believed incorrectly that zero divided by zero yielded a zero. He left fractions as 0/3 or 0/0 alone, without discovering the answer.

It was no small challenge for these ancient students of mathematics to overcome this difficulty. Two hundred years after Brahmagupta grappled with this issue, Jain mathematician Mahavira still struggled with division by zero. He claimed a number remained unchanged when it was divided by zero, a concept we now know is wrong. But he did correctly calculate that the square root of zero is zero.

The problems continued well into the twelfth century. Bhaskara, the leading Indian mathematician of his day, said that dividing zero by a quantity produces a quantity 'as infinite as the God Vishnu.' Yet, the Hindu decimal system proved successful in every other way. Its use spread to Persia, the Arabian empire and Europe to the west as China to the east.

Ironically, the actual symbol zero and its potential use were not discovered by mathematicians toiling over numbers. *Instead, the zero was revealed to ancient Vedics during deep meditation.* It is hard to imagine the development of any civilization, let alone scientific advancement, without the essential zero.

In fact, the entire roots of mathematics also originated in the *Vedas*, as a result of profound contemplation. Vedic mathematicians authored various theses and dissertations on the subject. Based on sixteen *sutras*, or formulae, this system was rediscovered between 1911 and 1918 by Sri Bharati Krsna Tirthaji (1884-1960). These treatises laid down the very foundations of algebra, algorithm, square roots, cube roots, various methods of calculation, in addition to the concept of zero.

Those who employ this striking method of problem solving find it far more systematic, coherent and unified than traditional mathematics. A mental tool for calculation, it encourages the development and use of intuition and innovation. However, the real beauty and effectiveness of this system cannot be fully appreciated without actually practicing it.

If you want to find the square of 45, you can employ the *Ekadhikena Purvena sutra* ('By one more than the one before'). The rule says since the first digit is 4 and the second one is 5, you will first have to multiply 4 (4+1), that is 4 x 5, which is equal to 20 and then multiply 5 with 5, which is 25. Viola! The answer is 2025. Now, you can employ this method to multiply all numbers ending with 5.

Vedic mathematics is so refined and precise that it is being taught in the most prestigious institutions worldwide. *It is even being employed by NASA scientists in the development of artificial intelligence!* It has bridged the gap between ancient wisdom and contemporary science. Nothing new has been discovered – only revisited.

For many, the zero is as much a spiritual symbol as it is a profound mathematical emblem and tool. We conceptualize the zero as a circle. It represents both everything and nothing simultaneously. The unbroken nature of the circle symbolizes boundless infinity.

Even the definition of the circle itself can be expressed in terms of infinity or nothing. You can see the circle as an undivided and never ending line – or as an 'infinite number of infinitely short lines.' The ends of the circle meet; the difference between the infinitely large and the infinitesimally small blurs.

Between zero and infinity lies probably the most famous number known to mankind. It's so famous, in fact, that it is recognizable merely by a symbol. That number is known as 'Pi.' Its definition is simple: the ratio of the circumference of a circle to its diameter. Its exact value is much more difficult to decipher, though. Pi is just a little more than three – and from the beginning, various estimates were used to designate it. Babylonians used 25/8 or 3.125; the Egyptians decided on 3.16.

Archimedes attempted for the first time to devise a method for calculating the number. He created a polygon with 96 sides – this approximating a circle – and placed Pi at 3.1418. But Johann Lambert argued in 1768 that the number was 'irrational.' It could not be expressed as the ratio of two numbers. Lambert also claimed that a repeating pattern could not be a decimal. And Pi has a repeating pattern.

More than 100 years later, Ferdinand Lindemann, in 1882, proved that Pi is 'transcendental.' It is a value that cannot be a solution to any algebraic equation. It is impossible to square a circle using a compass and a ruler, he said, referring to Archimedes's attempt.

But still, we try to find an exact value for this elusive number. The twentieth century brought the addition of a new tool – the computer. In 1949, using this high-tech instrument, mathematicians were able to determine the value of Pi to 2,037 decimal places. Nearly 50 years later, in 1997, a more powerful computer extended the value to a stunning 51,539,600,000 decimal places. While the sequence of these digits still appears random, the string of numbers '0123456789' appears in six different places in the number.

Amazingly advanced, the ancient Indian scholarly caste, the *Brahmin*, not only had calculated Pi to 32 decimals (and beyond, it appears), but had the number memorized! This intellectual group tightly guarded all of its knowledge, not wanting it to spread to other castes. While they would normally sing songs to memorize long decimals, when it came to Pi, these men disguised the number. They encrypted it into their devotional praises and hymns to Lord Sri Krishna.

In fact, the Vedic Numerical Codes were so intricately devised for this famous number that it contained three layers, or meanings. Using a system similar to numerology, these masters assigned number values to the consonant letters.

They chanted Pi – 32 decimal places of it, 3.14159265358697932384626433832792, by coding it in the following syllables when they chanted:

> *'Gopi Bhagyamadhuv Rata*
> *Srngisodadhi Sandhiga*
> *Khala Jeevitarvava Tava*
> *Galaddhalara Sangara'*

In the first line the carefully guarded code is: go=3, pi= 1, bha=4, ya=1, ma=5, dhu=9, ra=2, ta=6. The fist line conveys the first eight digits of Pi.

Not only did these masters chant the first 32 decimal places of Pi, it is said that within a secret Master Key of the first set, lay the keys that would unlock the second set of 32 decimal places. Within the second 32 places, moreover, was ... you guessed ... another master key to unlock the third set. This continued indefinitely. The *Brahmin* possessed a ticket to infinity.

The Vedic view of knowledge assumed that by acquiring transcendental knowledge you could also learn the intricate details of the material world around you. In the process of gathering and knowing the absolute truth, all relative truths manifested themselves. It appears Pi was not only a powerful mathematical tool, but a potent spiritual symbol as well.

Indeed, this violates our deep routed sense that spiritual wisdom and scientific knowledge lay on parallel linear lines. Now we see more clearly that with each new revelation in our Quest for Reality, the lines were never really parallel. Only our perception was skewed.

Follow me on a journey into the *Secrets of Reality* that is at once amazing and inspiring as together we discover that the knowledge of science and philosophy are not found on any linear spectrum, but only revealed on the circumference of the unbroken circle, for they are infinitely joined as one.

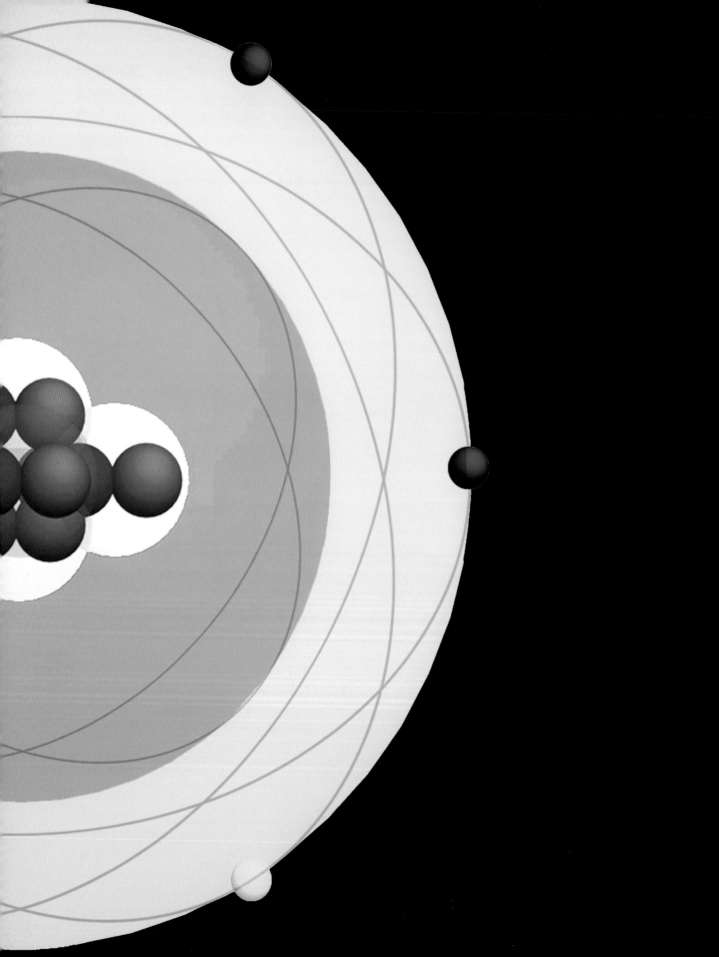

Nanocosm

For almost three centuries, the Newtonian thinkers had claimed the universal reality as orderly, predictable and continuous. Things flowed smoothly through space; energy came in an infinite range of amounts; light undulated in a continuous wave and there was nothing left to discover.

Yet within a generation, the world of classical physics was turned upside down by new anomalies of phenomena operating in the microscopic world of the physical reality or 'nanocosm.' In this unseen realm, nature revealed itself to be strange and nonlocal: the whole universe a network of time and space transcending interconnection.

The 'quantum revolution' that these anomalies generated is the one true revolutionary event in the whole history of science. To understand this we travel back to the dawn of the twentieth century and witness the birth of quantum theory which, over the next one hundred years, overthrew so many of the most deeply held notions about Reality.

Quantum Revolution

Clockwork Universe

The year is 1642; the world loses the greatest scientist up to that time – Galileo. But, in an ironic turn of fate, a baby is born, destined it seems to shake the very foundation of science and alter the course of the Western thought.

Isaac Newton was born premature on a cold Christmas Day – and though he never knew his father and mother remarried when he was two – he grew up to be arguably the most influential physicist the world has ever known. He not only designed an improved astronomical telescope, he showed that white light is made up of all the colors of the rainbow, and developed the idea that light is composed of a stream of particles called *corpuscles*. And he did all this by the age of 25!

Of course, looking back from our perspective, it all seems quite mundane. Indeed, his laws have stood the test of time and the scrutiny of experimentation through the centuries. Much of the explanation for the working of the physical world we see around us, we owe to Isaac Newton. In the 21st Century it seems more commonsense than radical. But his laws and explanations did, indeed, rock the world of science.

He showed that the laws of physics are universal. The same law of gravity, which makes an apple fall from a tree, is also the one that holds the Moon in its orbit. All moving objects obey the same laws of mechanics, including a ball that rolls down a hill.

Through the cogency of his laws, he explained motion, force, and gravity in a practical, applicable way that lent themselves to use. The laws have been utilized to explain everything from the way atoms and molecules bounce off each other, to how the moving parts of an engine interact, and what was required to put man on the Moon.

He described the mechanics of the material world, so convincingly in fact that he almost single handedly divided the world into matter and 'non-material' that spiritual, ethereal, realm. Before Newton, scientists actively meshed both spheres. After Newton, scientists studied physical matter, leaving the ethereal concerns for philosophers to contemplate. The chasm between the arenas was so large that it existed for more than three centuries after Newton's passing.

His world was a world of determinism. Everything from a weight oscillating on a spring to the motions of the planetary bodies represented systems that obeyed apparent laws of causality. Given the initial state of any system,

Sir Isaac Newton

Isaac Newton (1642-1727) was the founder of modern science and invented calculus. The idea of gravity came to him as he sat while contemplating how the Moon revolved around Earth and 'was occasioned by the fall of an apple.' This creative genius was sensitive to the slightest criticism, egotistical and suffered fits of depression. Doubtful of revealing his work in print, were it not for the persuasion of his friend Edmund Halley, the 'Principia Mathematica' would never have been published.

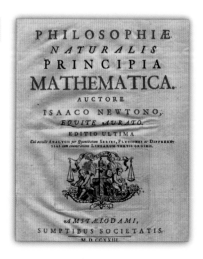

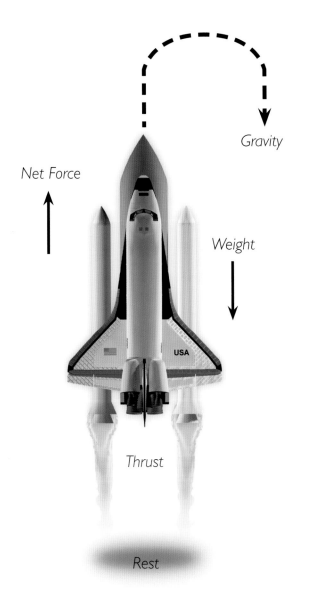

Net Force

Gravity

Weight

Thrust

Rest

I. Law of Inertia:

A body in motion will tend to stay in motion, and a body at rest will tend to stay at rest, unless acted upon by an outside force, such as friction.

II. Law of Acceleration:

The force acting on an object is equal to the object's mass multiplied by its acceleration.

III. Law of Action and Reaction:

For every action, there is an equal and opposite reaction.

IV. Universal Law of Gravitation:

The force of attraction between two objects is proportional to the product of their masses and inversely proportional to the square of the distance between them.

all later states of the system could be predicted with great precision. This eventually led to the pervasive belief that events of the world are predetermined, evolving orderly in time to a fixed destiny, much like a giant clock.

Newtonian physics was successful because his laws seemed to show that causality existed for virtually every system immediately perceivable, from billiard balls to automobiles, from clocks to eclipses. And where prediction was impractical, physicists still assumed that the system was causal.

Once the clock was wound up, events would unfold in an orderly and predictable sequence. Scientists and philosophers alike absorbed the idea of *causal determinism.* The theory was so ingrained in the thought of the day its influence could be seen in Jefferson's political ideas as laid out in American Declaration of Independence as well as in the doctrine of Puritan's determinism.

But, trouble loomed on the causal determinism sphere. Newtonian physics failed to adequately explain 'invisible processes': heat, sound, electricity or magnetism. And by the late 1800s dark clouds appeared on the Newtonian horizon.

Let There Be Light!

The failure of Newtonian physics to adequately explain the mechanics of magnetism, sound, electricity, heat and other invisible processes stumped scientists for nearly two hundred years. Worse yet, from a scientific viewpoint, it created a missing link in our understanding of the mechanics of the world.

James Maxwell would connect this link with his now famous set of four equations that bear his name. While Newton studied the 'seen', Maxwell riveted his attention to the 'unseen' and not yet fully examined world of magnetism and electricity. In fact, he married the two and much to his delight, out came light!

He built his work on the original ideas of Michael Faraday, who discovered the potentially immense power of electro-magnetism. Faraday had realized that pushing a magnet into a coil of wire connected to a meter to measure electric current caused the needle of the meter to flicker.

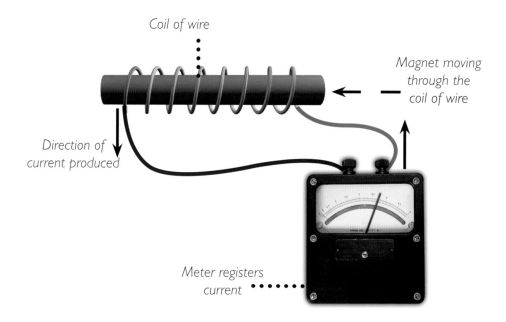

Coil of wire

Magnet moving through the coil of wire

Direction of current produced

Meter registers current

James Clerk Maxwell

James Clerk Maxwell (1831-1879) won Edinburgh Academy's medal for mathematics at 14 years of age. He was interested in just about all aspects of 19th – century physics. He proved that the rings of Saturn were made up of a myriad of small Moons in orbit around the planet; invented color photography; described the electromagnetism in classical terms and developed the mathematical description of light wave.

Michael Faraday

Michael Faraday (1791-1867) was the son of a poor blacksmith and had very little formal education. He had learnt the 'rudiments of reading, writing, and arithmetic' in a day school. Over the years, he invented the first electric motor and showed that magnetism could be converted to electricity. Not bad for someone with an eighth-grade education.

Maxwell revealed that light was, in essence, an electromagnetic wave. The light waves visible to the naked eye, in fact, are only a small portion of the electromagnetic spectrum, which ranges from the very short gamma radiation to the very long radio waves. A wavelength being defined as the distance between two successive peaks or troughs of the wave.

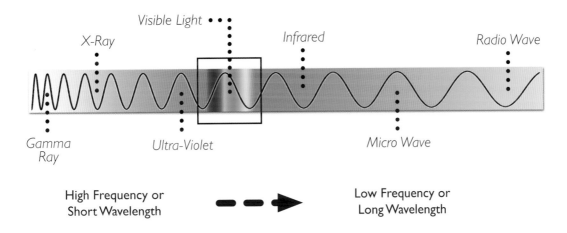

But the length of a wave mattered little in defining or studying their effects. For all waves, whether they be radio or light waves, he said, *always* traveled at the constant – if somewhat mind-boggling --speed of 186,000 miles per second. That's the equivalent of 670 million miles per hour.

Every problem involving electricity and magnetism now could be solved by using Maxwell's equations, just as every problem involving classical mechanics could be solved by using Newton's laws. Maxwell's work stood alongside Newton's as a pillar of scientific achievement. His laws concerning the behavior of light and other electromagnetic phenomena, coupled the visible physical world with the invisible. Or did it?

Pandora's Box

Physicists sat smugly in their 19th Century dominion, like kings surveying their realm, confident that the movement of all physical phenomena had once and for all been adequately explained.

Newton's clockwork mechanics and Maxwell's electro-magnetism were the stalwart twin pillars supporting a nearly comprehensive view of the physical world. There just remained a handful of i's to dot and a few t's to cross.

Then Max Planck leapt into the 20th Century and shattered the serenity and unwavering assuredness of the scientific world. His experiment with 'black bodies' opened up a Pandora's box, which failed to explain why these objects, which absorbed all electromagnetic radiation, glowed from red to white hot when heated. A hot black body in fact, emitted what scientists call, naturally enough, black body radiation. But the quandary for these physicists proved puzzling indeed. Once the body got hot, it was no longer black, because it then emitted visible light.

Classical theory stated that the electromagnetic spectrum of radiation was related to the body's temperature. It predicted, as the black body became hotter and hotter, it should emit huge amounts of energy in the highest frequency part of the spectrum, namely ultraviolet and beyond. But it didn't.

Confronted by the inexplicable phenomenon, the German physicist was reduced to a desperate remedy of solving the puzzle. 'What if the black body absorbed heat and emitted light in a discontinuous pattern?' he wondered. Radical thinking, perhaps, but definitely worth further investigation, he decided.

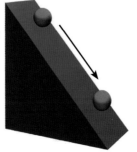 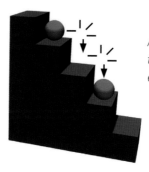

On a slope, the classical motion of the ball is continuous

Analogous to the discontinuous ball motion on steps: energy is emitted in chunks called 'quanta'

Accepting energy in small chunks he solved the puzzle of the black body radiation. Planck proposed that energy – which underlies all of nature -- was not continuous. It came instead in bursts, even 'packets.' Atoms emitted these bursts of energy, which he named *quanta* – from the Latin word for 'how much' -- not in continuous waves as was previously believed.

If the idea of 'packets' of energy is difficult to understand, consider this analogy. Imagine two balls being released, one down a flight of stairs, the other down a smooth slope. The ball descending the slope releases its energy in a continuous supply. However, the ball falling down the stairs releases its energy in jumps.

Quantum came out of a hot box. Now, energy, light, force and motion were 'quantized' and led to the 'quantum revolution.' Within a quarter of a century, the commonsense laws of science toppled like a house of cards. Replacing them were a seemingly bizarre set of rules, in which all the qualities of the subatomic world were precisely quantifiable.

Max Planck

Max Planck (1858-1947) started the quantum revolution in 1900, when he explained black body radiation in terms of light quanta. In 1918, he received the Nobel Prize for his scientific work. In school he excelled as a pianist and discussed the possibility of a musical career with a musician who told him that if he had to ask the question he should better study something else.

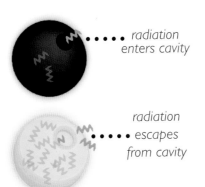

radiation enters cavity

radiation escapes from cavity

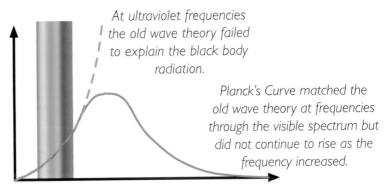

At ultraviolet frequencies the old wave theory failed to explain the black body radiation.

Planck's Curve matched the old wave theory at frequencies through the visible spectrum but did not continue to rise as the frequency increased.

Planck's Constant

Perhaps Max Planck is best known to the casual student of science for his mathematical ratio, which became known as Planck's constant. The scientist, in order to explain his theory of 'packets of energy', mathematically divided radiation into chunks or quanta. He assigned an energy, designated mathematically by the letter E, to each quantum. In turn, each quantum held a specific relationship to its wave frequency, which he called f. Planck calculated that the constant, shown as $\hbar = E/f$. (The $\hbar$ is called an 'h-bar').

Thus, this brilliant scientist proved that the particle's energy is proportional to its frequency. The relation between these two characteristics is surprisingly quite simple. Consider the frequency of violet light at one extreme of the visible spectrum. It's twice the frequency of the red light at the other end. So, by logical extension, a quantum of violet light possesses twice as much energy as a quantum of red light.

Planck's constant, as the name implies, is always unvarying. It is always equal to one quantum. A quantum equals an unimaginably small number: a billionth of a billionth of one (1). As small as that number is, it is not zero (0). If it were, you would not be able to sit in front of a fire. And, of course, the minute size of Planck's constant — and the quantum — means that these energy packets are not noticeable in your daily life.

Particles Of Light

Music fills the air at the Berlin Academy in the early 1920s. The harmonious and beautiful sounds of a piano and a violin echo the classics of chamber music. Two giant physicists are relaxing, creating these superb sounds and enjoying each other's company. The musicians are none other than: Albert Einstein and Max Planck. Einstein, absorbed by his violin, and Planck concentrating on his piano, may appear to us to be an odd couple in this setting. Indeed, though, this scene was not uncommon when the two were at the Academy.

The pair, however, did not limit the their collaboration to music, for Einstein continued Planck's study of quantum physics and, in fact, took it several steps farther. Earlier in Einstein's career, when this most famous of scientists was but a patent clerk in Switzerland, he had incorporated Planck's lumpy picture of wave energy into a description of light. He proposed that light was not composed of a wave. Instead, light was made up of *particles*, or in the words of the new physics, discrete particles. This idea was so new that it required a new word to describe these particles. Einstein christened them 'photons.'

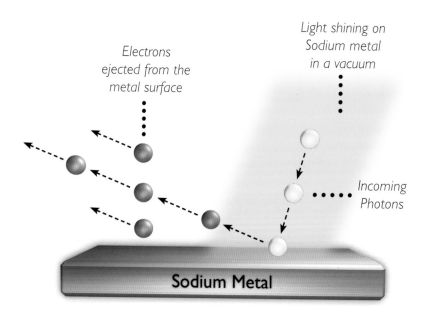

Einstein came to this conclusion after carefully studying the photoelectric effect, that is, the ability of a beam of light to cause a metal surface to emit electrons. Nineteenth century physics proved incapable of explaining this observable fact. However, by incorporating Planck's chunky picture of wave energy into a description of light, Einstein could account for this event.

Planck, at first, found Einstein's revelations difficult to accept. It was years before experiments actually confirmed Einstein's theories. But the confirmation of them resurrected Planck's quantum revolution. Quantum physics was harmonizing as well as Planck's and Einstein's duets.

Quantum Leap

The theories and revelations of Planck and Einstein gave birth to the Quantum Revolution. But quantum physics was only in its infancy. It would reach maturity with the developments of Joseph J. Thompson and Ernest Rutherford. Thompson envisioned the atom as a large, diffuse, positively charged chunk of material with electrons embedded in it like raisins tucked inside a bun.

Rutherford, a New Zealander, elaborated on Thompson's findings. He discovered the basic structure of the atom, which is familiar: a central positively charged nucleus surrounded by a cloud of negatively charged electrons. His model suggested that the electrons were 'in orbit' around the nucleus much like the way the planets orbit around the sun.

This proposal though didn't just redraw the picture of the atom. It threw into question long-standing theories. In the atomic world, any electrically charged particle which orbited in this manner should, according to the then standard laws, radiate away from the energy and spiral into the nucleus, causing the atom itself to collapse. If Rutherford's view was correct, what then was holding the atom together?

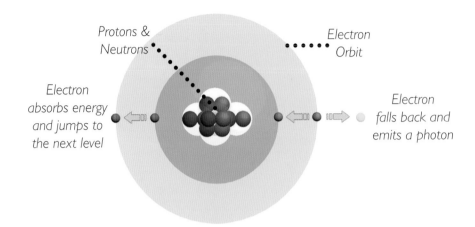

Protons &
Neutrons

Electron
Orbit

Electron
absorbs energy
and jumps to
the next level

Electron
falls back and
emits a photon

Young physicist Niels Bohr contributed the answer to this question and in the process established quantum physics as more – much more – than a series of mathematical parlor tricks.

Bohr described the orbits of electrons around the nucleus in layers like onion rings. He theorized that an electron jumped to any unfilled shell if it absorbed a quantum of energy. It could also fall back to an unfilled shell if it released a photon of energy. But Bohr added this contingent on the movement of subatomic particles: *the electron jumps from one unfilled shell to another but never traverses through the area between the two shells.* This discontinuous transition between quantum states eventually was labeled a 'quantum leap.'

This theory defies everything we know about the physical world. To illustrate this idea, we compared it to a ball bouncing down a flight of stairs. Under the terms of this theory, you never view the ball as it bounced from one step to the next. Yet somehow, in some strange way, it crosses that space to appear on the next step.

Bohr applied Planck's idea of quantization to atomic structure and stunningly accounted not only for the stability of the atom, but the atom's ability to emit light. And, in the process, the seemingly inexplicable quantum not only ruled the volatile realm of light, but now the concrete world as well, which includes the matter that we are all made of.

Ernest Rutherford

Ernest Rutherford (1871-1937) won the Nobel Prize in Chemistry in 1908 for 'his investigations into the disintegration of the elements and the chemistry of radioactive substances.' With this prestigious award, he delighted in telling his friends that he made the fastest transformation possible: the one from physicist to chemist.

Niels Bohr

Niels Bohr (1885-1962) was Professor of Theoretical Physics at Copenhagen University. He was the first to apply quantum physics to a description of the atom. Recognition of his work on the structure of atoms came with the award of Nobel Prize for 1922. He was born on his mother's 25th birthday. Besides being an excellent soccer player he studied texts ahead of the class finding errors in them.

Democritus

Greek philosopher Democritus (c.400 B.C.) proposed that all matter was composed of indivisible particles called atoms. Very little is known of his life but we know his travels took him to Egypt and Persia and it is suggested that he traveled to Babylon, India and Ethiopia as well.

Ancient Vedic Atomic Theory

Ancient and atomic are words not usually used in the same phrase. Pre-historic Indian Vedic atomic theory was far more advanced than those forwarded later by Greek philosophers – that not only everything was made up of parimanu (Sanskrit word for atom) but there were a variety of parimanu as different classes of elements then believed to exist, namely, earth, water, air and fire. Above all, each parimanu had a peculiar property, which was the same as the class of matter it belonged to and an inherent urge made one parimanu combine with another.

Nature's Trick

On Mondays, Wednesdays and Fridays light behaves like waves, on Tuesdays, Thursdays and Saturdays like particles, and like nothing at all on Sundays.

— Sir William Bregg (1920)

While Einstein's discovery of the photoelectric effect was indeed brilliant – he won a Nobel Prize for his find, what did it do to the findings of the famous double-slit experiment performed a century earlier? Had the nature of light changed in a century?

The year was 1800, and Thomas Young, a medical doctor turn physicist, cut two narrow slits in a piece of opaque material. He shines a small candlelight through the slits onto a screen beyond. What he expected to find, according to the knowledge of the day, was two bands of light on the second screen – one for each slit. This would confirm that light was composed of particles. Imagine his surprise, when the results shattered his hypothesis. The screen displayed a series of bright and dark bands of varying intensity instead.

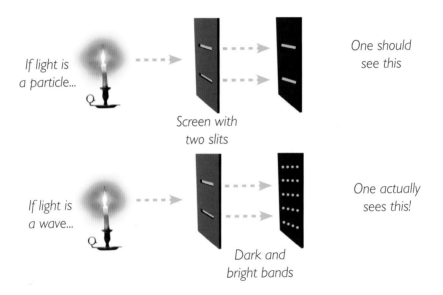

If light is a particle...

Screen with two slits

One should see this

If light is a wave...

Dark and bright bands

One actually sees this!

Thomas Young

Thomas Young (1773 -1829) was a truly multi-talented individual. A Professor of Physics at Cambridge University, he discovered the cause of astigmatism of the eye and proposed the three-color theory of perception. And he is also remembered for the monumental task of deciphering the Rosetta stone, which allowed Egyptologists to translate hieroglyphics.

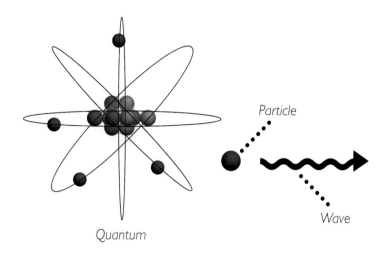

Quantum

Particle

Wave

This could only occur if light spread as a wave, much like the ripples on a pond when the water is disturbed. Where the ripples from each of the two slits were in step – that is their peaks matched, they made a bright band. If they were out of step, one peak crossed another's trough, they left a dark band.

Such a revelation for an experiment that appeared so elementary! The double-slit experiment proved that light travels as a wave. But wait! Didn't we just say that Einstein won his Nobel Prize for showing that light is composed of … particles? Paradoxical, now, isn't it?

So, you may be wondering, who is correct, Young or Einstein? It might surprise you to learn that both scientists are correct. Einstein's photoelectric effect at the start of the 20th century brought the wave or particle debate full circle.

Scientists were finally accepting the dual nature of light. Indeed confronting these facts demand we shed our intuition that we classify something as either a particle or a wave. We must come to terms that entities in the microscopic world, could in fact be *both*. And that is exactly the nature of light. It is both a wave and a particle. And thus, Nature's 'trick' evolved into the 'central mystery' of the quantum theory and became known as 'the wave-particle duality.'

Quantum Magic

It might look crazy, but it really is sound.

-- Albert Einstein, critiquing the doctoral thesis of Louis de Broglie

If light were both particle and wave, what other matter may lie out there that contained a dual nature? Were there other entities that behaved as particles part of the time and as waves at others? These were the questions that Louis de Broglie kept asking. De Broglie, a graduate student, began his search in the early 1920s to answer this question.

Einstein's idea that matter and energy were interchangeable, through the equation of $E=mc^2$ had become fairly well accepted by the 1920s. De Broglie, who by the way, was a French Prince, used this thesis as the foundation of his work. Since matter and light are both forms of energy, de Broglie reasoned, and light can be understood as both a particle and a wave, he suggested that all forms of matter must be regarded as being both particle and wave.

He developed a mathematical equation that explained the wave-particle duality of light and extended it to all forms of matter. In fact, his equation, in a nutshell, showed that a wavelength, designated by λ, associated with a photon multiplied by its momentum, notated as p, equaled Planck's constant.

$$\hbar: \lambda \times p = \hbar$$

De Broglie proposed that the 'wave equation' as he called it, was universally true. Every particle – an electron or anything else, for that matter – could be associated with what he labeled, a 'matter wave.'

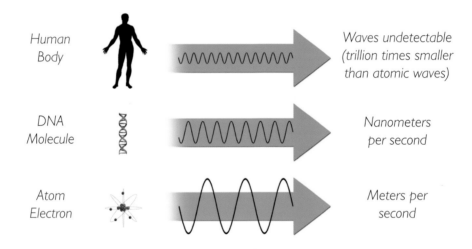

Human Body		Waves undetectable (trillion times smaller than atomic waves)
DNA Molecule		Nanometers per second
Atom Electron		Meters per second

But then he confronted the next natural question. If that were the case, why could we not see the 'waviness' of such everyday objects as people, houses, or even grains of sand on the beach? de Broglie had an answer. In large macroscopic items, the wave-like character of the object is virtually undetectable.

Remember, now, that Planck's constant itself is only one billionth of a billionth of one. De Broglie's equation establishes the wavelength of an object as being equal to Planck's constant divided by its momentum related to mass, the wave would only be detected for items that were indeed miniscule.

Those professors reviewing de Broglie's dissertation struggled with this concept. Finally, in frustration, they sent the paper to Einstein and asked his opinion. Einstein's response: 'It may look crazy, but it really is sound.' Not many people can thank Einstein for aid in receiving their doctorate!

If Einstein's recommendation were not enough, de Broglie's ideas were vindicated in 1927, when beams of electrons were demonstrated to embody the dual wave-particle nature, after being subject to an experiment very similar to the double-slit revelation Young performed with light. This proved that everything in the quantum realm is particle and wave simultaneously.

De Broglie added a new element to the quantum fray. But compared to the orderly world created by Newton in the 17th century, this world of quantum physics seemed more magic than science.

Louis de Broglie

Louis de Broglie (1892-1987) a French Prince, owes the awarding of his doctorate in physics to Albert Einstein. When his professors were confronted with his hypothesis that all matter must be composed of both wave and particle, they sent his research off to Einstein, who certified it sound. In 1929, de Broglie was awarded the Nobel Prize for discovery of the wave nature of electrons.

God's Dice

Certainly, nothing in the Newtonian world equips us to understand the unfolding of the events in the early 20th century in the quantum world. The dual nature of both light and the quantum appears diametrically opposed to the world we experience on a daily basis.

But just when you think that events and revelations could not seem any more bizarre, yet another physicist enters the arena with yet another unimaginable hypothesis that ….

Max Born was not satisfied with the 'dual nature' explanation that his colleagues were espousing. He turned to mathematics to define the truth. In doing so, Born determined that 'the wave was not the particle.' The wave, instead, was a wave of *probability*. He utilized it not as an object, but as a function to predict the probable location of a single electron.

The probability of the location of the electron – as expressed through the language of mathematics – formed a bell-shaped curve, Born concluded. The position with the highest probability – which would be at the top of the curve – is the *most likely place to find the particle*. However, there exists an entire region of places along the curve where there would be a considerably good chance of pinpointing the particle as well. It mattered not how the wave shook and danced, there had to be a particle along that trajectory somewhere, Born reasoned.

Compare the work of Born to your ability, or more appropriately, inability to predict with absolute certainty the final resting place of a marble on a roulette wheel. While it's one thing to be uncertain about a game of chance, it's quite another to encounter this uncertainty when it comes to the fundamental workings of the world.

This was too much even for some quantum physicists to accept. How could probability be a characteristic that was built into the universe? Something Einstein hated, famously commenting, 'I cannot believe that God plays dice.'

But, Einstein was wrong. Because, indeed, Born's work was sound. If Newton's causal determination created a revolution that reverberated throughout the worlds of science, philosophy, and religion, Born created a second revolution, his dance of the electron, which annihilated causal determinism and the Newtonian notion of a 'clockwork universe.'

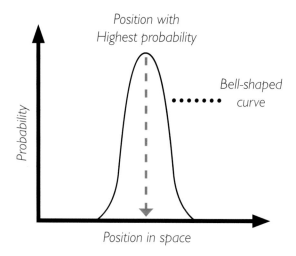

Position with
Highest probability

Bell-shaped
curve

Probability

Position in space

Max Born

Max Born (1882-1970) was Tait Professor of Natural Philosophy in Edinburgh and received a Nobel Prize in 1954 for his ground breaking research in quantum mechanics, especially in relation for his statistical interpretation of wave function.

Uncertainty is Certain

Probability thoroughly penetrated quantum physics. Indeed, the deeper the physicists probed into the nanocosm, the farther their explanations deviated from the 'real world' we experience daily as part of the predictable, orderly world of Newtonian physics. Their investigations only led to uncertainty.

Uncertainty reigned supreme, or so it seemed to German scientist Werner Heisenberg. In fact, it was so ingrained in the quantum realm that it was implicit in the equations describing the behavior of things, such as electrons. Position is a property of a particle, Heisenberg stated, while momentum a property of wave. He studied the mathematical relationship between the speed and position of a particle and came up with the uncertainty principle.

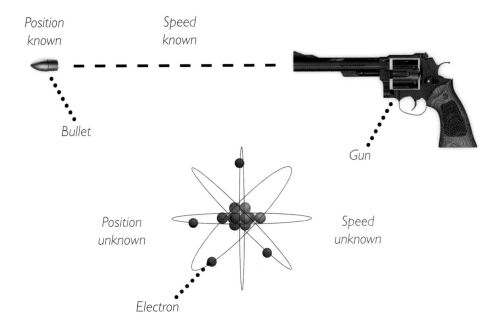

He explained it this way: A scientist, using mathematics, could theoretically calculate the speed and position – at any given moment – of a bullet fired from a gun. That was not possible with an electron – or any other quantum entity for that matter -- as it hurtled through space. You could either know the speed or the position of the electron, but not both.

Perhaps more than any other discovery, Heisenberg's uncertainty principle signaled the end to both the Newtonian model of the universe in which all events could be determined with an uncanny accuracy and Einstein's reasoning. *The uncertainty principle captured the heart of quantum reality.*

Mental Paradox

As long as we insist on viewing the quantum realm using our ordinary perspective, we are destined to see only a single dimension at any given time. And trying to distinguish the attributes of a wave from a particle could be hazardous to your mental health.

But, thanks to the efforts of Niels Bohr, that is not how we necessarily need to look at things. It doesn't matter if we can't measure both motion and position simultaneously, he said. Can we see both sides of a coin at the same time? he asked. This 'one-aspect-or-the-other-but-not-both-simultaneously' led to the Principle of Complementarity.

And here's a perfect example of this principle at work: When you look at the image, what do you see initially: the goblet or the silhouette of the two faces? Notice that you will see one image and then the other, but not both at the same time. This inability to see both seems to be a fundamental paradox.

Keep looking at the illustration and switch your concentration from the goblet to the faces. Your consciousness naturally begins to incorporate the inherent duality of the image. The strangeness of quantum reality begins, albeit slowly, to make some sense.

Both waves and particles define what an electron is, in very much the same way that both sides of a coin define that item. Complementarity helps us to accept our innate limits of perception and measurement in the quantum domain.

The fundamental structure of the universe, it seemed, operated in ways that were both mysterious and profound at the same time.

Midas Touch

Perhaps not since the Newtonian laws of motion had any scientific theory profoundly affected our vision of the world. If everything around us is composed of quanta – those seemingly 'magical' subatomic parts that change their form from wave to particle when being observed with human eyes – how could we possibly trust our senses again?

The quantum wave function, scientists consistently showed, collapsed into a particle when it was being watched, effectively illustrating the maxim, 'To observe is to disturb.' It became totally impossible to separate the observer from the observed.

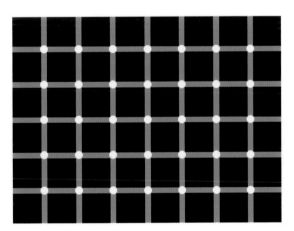

Let's turn to what we call optical illusions to try to understand the full implications of this knowledge. Stare at any one of the white dots on the image on the page. As you concentrate on one white spot, your eye catches black dots dancing around the diagram. Now, switch your gaze to one of those black dots you caught a glimpse of. What happens? Yes, they immediately turn white again! No matter how long you stare, or at what angle you approach the image, you'll never be able to capture that black dot and keep it black! This optical illusion shows how the simple act of observation affects the quantum system.

Just like Midas, the legendary king who never knew the feel of silk because everything he touched turned to gold, we can never experience quantum reality. Everything we observe turns to matter.

Wonderful Copenhagen

Niels Bohr remained unperturbed by the paradoxical behavior of quantum physics, even if it led some of his contemporaries to throw up their hands in exasperation.

Working in Copenhagen, Bohr and several colleagues, based their interpretation to include all the fundamental ideas of Heisenberg and Born. They integrated the ideas of uncertainty, complementarity, probability and the wave function, into a coherent system, which was called The Copenhagen Interpretation. What we choose to measure and the act of measuring it affects the nature of Reality.

Here's what the Interpretation said:

Imagine a box empty except for one electron. It exists as a wave filling the box. The moment we look at the box, the 'wave function collapses,' that is, the wave transforms into a particle, at a certain location. Quanta travel as waves, but arrive as particles as in the double-slit experiment.

Now, imagine dividing the box – without looking (for we know our observing the electron would transform it from a wave to a particle). As long as we didn't look into that box, according to the Copenhagen Interpretation, the wave fills the two halves of the box, even if they're separated by light years! It's only when we look into one side of the box or the other the wave function collapses, instantaneously, and the electron 'decides' which half to inhabit.

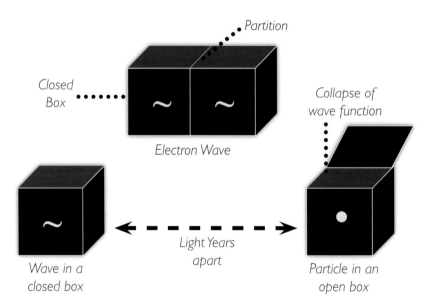

Partition

Closed Box

Collapse of wave function

Electron Wave

Wave in a closed box

Light Years apart

Particle in an open box

The idea that the electron is in both halves of the box at the same time is based on probability and leads us quite naturally to the paradox, supported by Heisenberg's uncertainty principle, that somehow the electron 'knows' in which half of the box to reside, even if the halves are separated by light years.

Bohr and his colleagues seemed to create rational sense of the inseparability inherent in quantum mechanics. This, however, proved to be the straw that broke the camel's back. Some respected physicists challenged the Copenhagen Interpretation with thought experiments.

Cat's Nine Lives

To prove the absurdity of Bohr's Copenhagen Interpretation, physicist Erwin Schrödinger created this thought experiment:

Imagine a cat enclosed in a windowless box. In addition to the cat was what he called a 'diabolical device' in the form of a radioactive source, along with a Geiger counter, a hammer and a sealed glass flask containing a poison gas. As the radioactive matter decayed, the Geiger counter triggered a device, which dropped the hammer, and in turn broke the flask, releasing the poison gas and killing the feline.

He postulated the quantum theory assigned a 50 percent chance of the radioactive decay occurring in an hour. This meant, he said, that once an hour had passed, odds were even that the cat was alive. Similarly, the odds were 50/50 that the cat was dead.

If you were to follow the logic of the Copenhagen Interpretation, peer into the box, you would be staring at a feline that was half dead and half alive – a superimposition of the two possible outcomes. But in reality, you will discover a cat that is either fully alive or completely dead.

This thought experiment proved his point, Schrödinger said. How could a cat possibly be both alive and dead simultaneously?

But Bohr retorted with an equally logical explanation: It was nothing more than the equivalent of the coherent superposition of the two wave functions. As soon as you open the box, your observing the cat collapsed the superimposition of the two wave functions into a single one, making the cat entirely alive or fully dead. *Human consciousness* is what collapses the cat's dichotomous state into a single one.

The complementarity principle further lessened the absurdity of the cat in the box as a half-alive, half-dead creature. The coherent superposition is an abstraction, which ultimately means the cat can indeed exist as both alive and dead.

The experiment highlights that there is a boundary existing between our view of everyday objects and the quantum world of very small objects. The boundary effectively disappears, however, when crossed.

'Spooky' Action

Schrödinger's 'cat experiment' was not the only challenge to the growing paradoxes of quantum physics. In the same year as he created his hypothetical cat, Einstein – along with Podolsky and Rosen – devised what came to be known as the EPR Paradox. This proposal, so named for the first initial of each of the three physicists' last names, highlighted what they believed to be the absurdity of quantum mechanics, namely indeterminism or nonlocality.

'How could information between particles possibly be passed instantaneously when light years apart,' the trio questioned, *'when nothing travels faster than the speed of light?'* In Einstein's words, this was 'spooky action at a distance.' The group intended to disprove Bohr's Copenhagen Interpretation by identifying apparent paradoxes in the theory.

They proposed the following thought experiment:

Since we cannot simultaneously measure certain sets of properties in a single particle, perhaps we could measure the quantities with the aid of a second particle – one whose properties in some way are linked to the first.

This thought experiment remained just that until 1965, when John Bell, a physicist at the European Organization for Nuclear Research (CERN) in Switzerland, showed how the EPR proposal might be carried out in reality using a brilliant mathematical proof. Bell demonstrated that either the quantum universe was non-objective, or it was 'nonlocal' with the instantaneous action-at-a-distance between the two particles.

Nearly 20 years after Bell's proof, another scientist, Alain Aspect, and his team of researchers, performed what may turn out to be one of the most significant experiments of the 20th century. They proved that subatomic particles – like electrons and photons – were, indeed, able to 'communicate' with each other. If this were not bizarre enough, this communication could occur regardless of the distance separating them – 10 feet or 10 billion miles!

Aspect's team produced a series of twin photons by heating calcium atoms with lasers. The photon then traveled in opposite directions through 6.5 meters of pipe, and passed through special filters. These filters directed them toward one of two possible polarization analyzers. The length of time it took the filters to switch from one analyzer to another was 30 billionths of a second less than it took light to travel the entire 13 meter length separating the two photons.

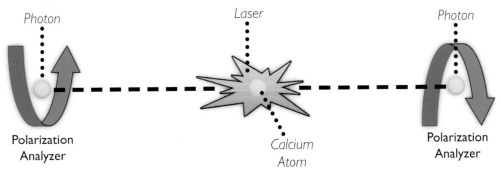

Photon   Laser   Photon

Polarization Analyzer   Calcium Atom   Polarization Analyzer

Each photon was still able to communicate its angle of polarization with its twin – even more swiftly than the speed of light!

The twin particles – despite their physical distance – always remained 'entangled' and 'knew' what the other was doing.

If any person considered this an anomaly, all doubt was removed in the 1990s when researchers repeated the experiment, this time using fiber optics. Scientists in Geneva sent twin photons speeding along a 10-kilometer fiber optic cable. And, yes, the 'communication' between the particles displayed nonlocality again.

Physicists worldwide were forced to sit up and pay attention. This instantaneous action at a distance, or nonlocality, violated Einstein's imposed limit on the speed of the universe, which was the speed of light. These results suggested the existence of *faster-than-the-speed-of-light* communication. Had Einstein been alive he would no doubt have finally admitted defeat.

Alain Aspect

Alain Aspect (1947 -) is the Carnegie Centenary Professor at Strathclyde and Chair of Atom Optics at the Laboratoire Charles Fabry of the Institute of Theoretical and Applied Optics at the University of Paris Sud, France. He confirmed the statistical quantum predictions and ruled out Einstein's view of reality. To paraphrase, a particle falling in the woods does not make a sound if there is no one to hear it. Strange – but true!

What a monumental milestone in the history of science! Once again, scientists shifted their perspective. Old laws crashed down around them as the very foundation of science shook mightily.

This was much like two people in different parts of the world, playing 'quantum cards.' For instance, each time the person in New York drew a card from the deck, the person in London also drew the same card. Again and again this turned to be true, even when the cards were drawn precisely at the same moment. Furthermore, the cards remain 'entangled' no matter how far apart the decks were moved!

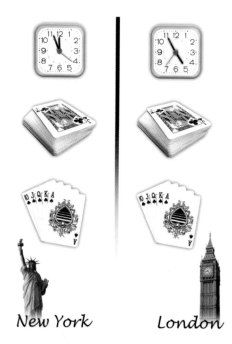

New York   London

Without a doubt the Aspect Experiment shifted our fundamental understanding of reality every bit as much as Newton's laws and Einstein's theories did. Some of our most cherished – and most widely accepted – ideas concerning reality, this experiment showed, were, in fact, mistaken! The equations governing the behavior of the objects we see and use everyday, from items as small as a grain of sand, to a football or even to the movements of the planets in our solar system, were absolutely meaningless in the quantum world.

John Bell

John Bell (1928-1990) was an Irish physicist. He was the recipient of the Hughes Medal of the Royal Society, the Dirac Medal of the Institute of Physics and the Heineman Prize of the American Physical Society. He investigated quantum theory in the greatest depth and established what the theory can tell us about the nature of the physical reality.

Beyond the Quantum

Instantaneous communication broke the existing laws of physics and was, indeed, too 'weird' for some physicists to accept. Could it be possible that this was not the proper explanation for the phenomenon researchers encountered?

Irish born David Bohm considered this as a possibility. Influenced as much by the Eastern philosopher, J. Krishnamurti as Einstein, Bohm theorized that instead faster-than-the-speed-of-light communication, these subatomic particles were not really separate entities after all. What if the separateness were only an illusion, and they were, in fact, the same aspect of a deeper fundamental reality.

Bohm suggested that perhaps there existed a nonlocal level of reality beyond the quantum. What we viewed as two separate photons, for example, referring back to the Aspect Experiment, could possibly be two perspectives of one photon.

His landmark work on plasmas – gas containing a high density of particles – found, much to his amazement, that subatomic particles were not independent units, as every scientist assumed. Their behavior instead strongly suggested they were part of an interconnected whole.

Bohm called this whole, the quantum potential, a field existing beyond the quantum level and which pervaded all space. According to this thinker, all points in space became equal to all other points in space. Location, in effect, ceased to exist.

He compared this concept – foreign to most physicists – as looking at one fish in an aquarium on two separate television monitors. Each monitor showed one fish from different angles. That however, did not mean these cameras were looking at two fish. If you viewed both monitors, Bohm said, not knowing you were viewing only one fish, you would assume that you were seeing two sea creatures acting in synchronized instant communication.

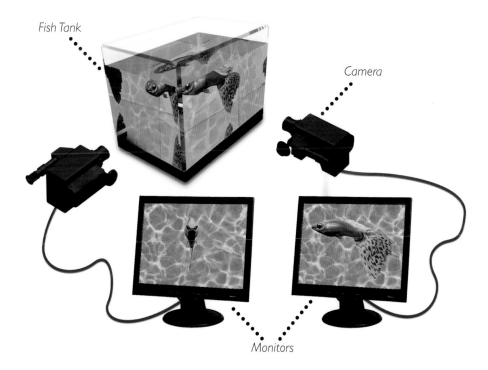

Fish Tank

Camera

Monitors

This led Bohm to a highly unorthodox conclusion: Particles, such as electrons appeared as separate entities. They were, however, on a level of deeper reality– a level analogous to the aquarium- they were actually just different aspects of a deeper fundamental 'something.'

In the quantum landscape, all semblance of location ceases to exist, not because the particles are communicating, but because their separateness is an *illusion* and they are aspects of a deeper fundamental reality.

Invisible Ink

Bohm's ideas took 'spooky' to a whole new level. Most mainstream scientists simply ignored his ideas for nearly 30 years from the 1950s to the 1980s.

Thankfully, the experiments of John Bell and Alain Aspect revived Bohm's theory. His ground breaking theory of 'wholeness and the implicate order' proposed a new model of reality that was nothing short of a revolutionary challenge to physics.

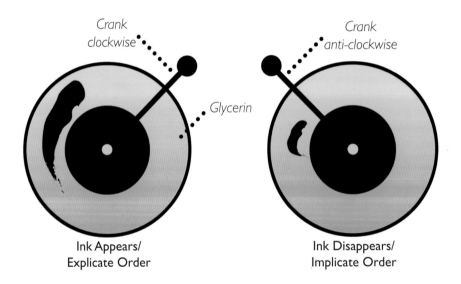

His 'quantum leap' in thinking occurred while he watched a BBC television program. The show featured a specially designed jar containing a large rotating cylinder. There was a narrow space between the cylinder and the jar was filled with glycerin. A drop of ink floated motionless in the glycerin.

When the cylinder was turned in a counter-clockwise direction, the drop of ink spread out through the syrupy glycerin and disappeared. When the handle was turned in the opposite direction – clockwise - the ink slowly came back together and formed a droplet.

Bohm used this phenomenon to explain that the order around us can be either enfolded, or *implicate*, illustrated by the invisible drop of ink or unfolded, or *explicate*, shown in the re-formed droplet.

The level of reality in which the particles appear separate – the level in which we live daily – is the explicate order. There exists, however, a deeper substratum of reality, where separateness vanishes and all things appear as a part of an unbroken whole. This he labeled the implicate order. Bohm's insightful theory offers an entire new view of the interconnectedness and the undivided wholeness of the quantum world.

Quantum physics is not just a wild idea. The revolution started by Planck and Einstein – the physics of the quantum theory – the exploration of microscopic quantities of matter – has found that it does, indeed, matter.

David Bohm

David Bohm (1917-1994) Born in Wilkes-Barre, Pa., this monumental thinker studied under Einstein and Oppenheimer. One of the world's greatest physicists of quantum mechanics also possessed a keen insightful philosophical vision. He was just as deeply influenced by J. Krishnamurti, as he was by his mentor, Einstein. Bohm died in London where he was serving as Professor of Theoretical Physics.

Subatomic World

Into the Atom

Physicists of the early twentieth century were finding themselves to be more than scientists. They were explorers and conquerors of a strange, new frontier. These individuals may have begun their trip to the heart of the atom as scientists, but they returned from their trek with wondrous tales of an unknown and unchartered 'land' every bit as foreign as those encountered by Christopher Columbus or Marco Polo.

On their maiden voyage in the quantum world, scientists originally believed that the atom was the smallest indivisible particle of matter. Yet subsequent journeys – especially those taken throughout the mid-1930s revealed a 'secret' infrastructure of this tiny building block of all objects. It was composed of electrons, protons and neutrons. And physicists believed that all territories of this extraordinary, unique environment had been visited.

But another generation of pioneers would follow and make some even more startling finds about the subatomic world. With the aid of particle accelerators, or as they were picturesquely dubbed initially, atom smashers, scientists learned more about the infrastructure of the atom. Remarkably, it appeared more magical than scientific!

The components of the neutron, proton and electron defy Newton's Laws of Matter. And while many scientists had likened the orbit of the electron to the nucleus of the atom to the planets around the Sun, there proved to be at least one fundamental difference. An electron revolves 720 degrees in order to make one complete revolution.

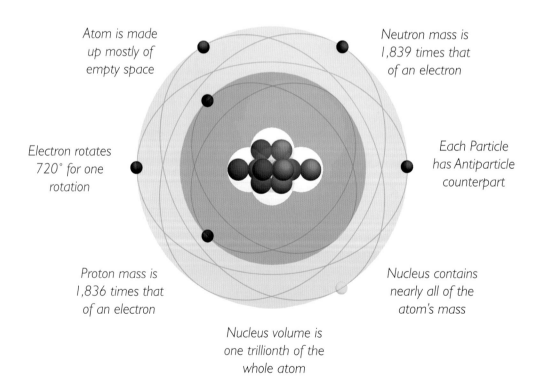

Atom is made up mostly of empty space

Neutron mass is 1,839 times that of an electron

Electron rotates 720° for one rotation

Each Particle has Antiparticle counterpart

Proton mass is 1,836 times that of an electron

Nucleus contains nearly all of the atom's mass

Nucleus volume is one trillionth of the whole atom

But the stunning revelations don't end there. The facts amass until you have a truly unbelievable picture of another world operating at a level too tiny to view with the naked eye, ruled by a set of laws yet to be decoded.

The nucleus of an atom, for example, comprises more than 99.9 percent of the atom's mass, yet one trillionth of its volume. Composed of positively charged protons and electrically neutral neutrons, each of these particles is about 2,000 times as massive as an electron.

The nucleus usually contains as many neutrons as protons, but there are atoms that contain more neutrons than protons. This creates an unstable center and the atom gives off emissions called radioactivity.

Equally perplexing to these pioneering scientists was the discovery that the majority of the atom's volume was nothing more than cloud of negatively charged electrons that literally possess no dimension!

But that's only the beginning of this fantastic voyage. The science of the infinitely miniscule reveals the most fundamental building blocks of matter were nearly surreal, with an illusory quality. An atom is virtually empty space, with a total size of 1/100,000,000 cm. Yet inside this cloud-like structure electrons vibrate and move at tremendous speed.

To give you some idea of the proportional qualities of this amazing particle of the universe, let's create an analogy that is more recognizable to our senses. Imagine the nucleus enlarged to the size of a golf ball. That would mean the atom itself were the size of the Earth. And the electron inside the nucleus? Proportionately, it would be the size of a grain of rice whizzing around in orbit. *Comparably, the total atomic mass of a 70 kg or 154 pound human being would be as big as the tip of a needle!* This is, indeed, nearly impossible for our minds to fathom because everything at our level of existence possesses dimension.

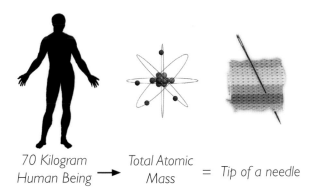

70 Kilogram Human Being → *Total Atomic Mass* = *Tip of a needle*

Understanding nature at its deepest and most intimate level has shattered our concept of solid objects and frankly left some of the greatest scientific minds bewildered and certainly awestruck-not words commonly used in the scientific process.

Yet, we're still not through with our journey into the heart of the subatomic world. It gets even more bizarre the deeper you look. Consider the phenomenon of barrier penetration called tunneling. Under certain circumstances the subatomic particles can pass through seemingly impenetrable barriers. This occurs in the case of household aluminum wiring. A thin insulating layer of aluminum oxide frequently builds up between the two twisted wires that make up household electrical cabling. This should stop the flow of the electric current. The electrons, though, easily tunnel across, maintaining the flow of electricity.

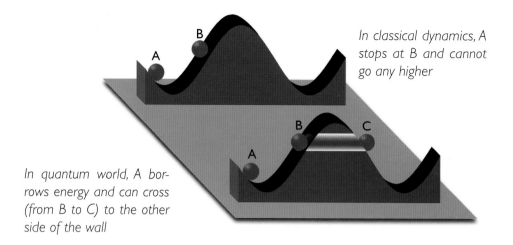

In classical dynamics, A stops at B and cannot go any higher

In quantum world, A borrows energy and can cross (from B to C) to the other side of the wall

Protons and neutrons are composed of even smaller units. Collectively known as nucleons, each proton and neutron is composed of quarks. And quarks, together with several types of leptons, constitute fermions – the foundation of matter. Another inhabitant of the microscopic landscape, the boson, transmits forces among them.

Now you may be wondering how scientists can say with any confidence that electrons and quarks are the fundamental building blocks of matter? If the history of physics is any indication, scientists in the future may discover that inside these tiny subatomic parts are even smaller parts, much like the progressively smaller Russian dolls are nested inside the larger one. Quite frankly, we can't make any guarantees. The most we can say is that with today's most advanced experiments, there is no hint of a deeper structure.

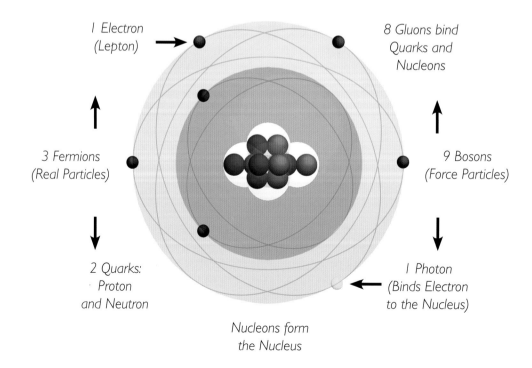

1 Electron (Lepton)

8 Gluons bind Quarks and Nucleons

3 Fermions (Real Particles)

9 Bosons (Force Particles)

2 Quarks: Proton and Neutron

1 Photon (Binds Electron to the Nucleus)

Nucleons form the Nucleus

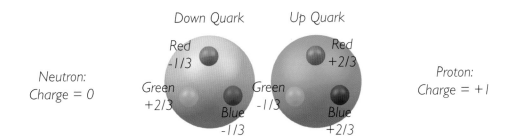

Down Quark   Up Quark

Neutron: Red   Red   Proton:
Charge = 0   -1/3   +2/3   Charge = +1
Green   Green
+2/3   -1/3
Blue   Blue
-1/3   +2/3

Quark Model

The word quark comes from a line in James Joyce's novel Finnegan's Wake: 'Three quarks for Muster Mark.'The standard quark model says that each nucleon is composed of three quarks.The quarks have a property similar to an electric charge, which occurs in three varieties, not two.These varieties are labeled using the names of colors- Red, Blue and Green -purely for convenience.There is always one quark of each color in a nucleon.A nucleon has two 'down' quarks with a charge of −1/3, and an 'up' quark, with a charge of +2/3 giving it no charge.A proton has two 'up' quarks and one 'down' quark, giving an overall charge of +1. 'Up' and 'down' are arbitrary names given by physicists.

Nature's Glue

Infinitesimally small subatomic particles speed around the core of the atom's nucleus at dizzying speeds. But what exactly keeps these tiny particles within their orbits? Why don't they just skyrocket out of control and go flying haphazardly anywhere they please? The best answer at the moment is nuclear glue. Japanese physicist Hideki Yukawa developed this theory in the 1930s and identified this glue-like force as one of the fundamental powers under which the universe operates.

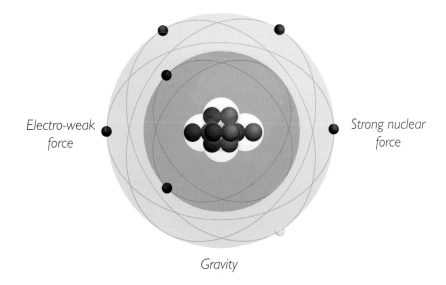

Electro-weak   Strong nuclear
force   force

Gravity

And, yes, there is more than one 'force' out there. Before you think that the existence of an invisible power holding particles in orbit is more fantasy than fact, consider the existence of gravity. Have you ever seen gravity? No, but every one of us has experienced its effects. We've seen apples fall from trees, watched babies drop their milk bottles, dropped a plate and watch it break into pieces as it hits the floor.

Surprisingly, gravity, whose strength keeps our feet firmly planted on the ground is the weakest of the three known forces in the universe today. The third power is electro-magnetism, which keeps the protons apart, since like charges repel. Thanks to this interplay between repulsive electromagnetic force and the attractive strong nuclear force, the nucleus is stable.

Radioactivity exists because the nuclear force in this instance is weak. Many, in fact, believe that the electromagnetic and weak nuclear powers are thought to be different aspects of the same force, now commonly called 'the electro-weak force.'

These 'invisible' forces at work in the universe are shrouded in mystery and secrecy. Scientists still have not sorted out the existence of these forces and their relationship to each other. Perhaps they were unified at one time in a hot, young, universe, less than a trillionth of a second prior to the beginning of time and split during the Big Bang. Indeed, perhaps these mystical forces actually put the 'Bang' in The Big Bang.

Hideki Yukawa

In 1935 Hideki Yukawa, a theoretical physicist was the first Japanese to win the Nobel Prize for the explanation of the nuclear glue. In 1940 he won the Imperial Prize of the Japan Academy, in 1943 the Decoration of Cultural Merit from the Japanese government. He joined 10 other leading scientists and intellectuals in signing the Russell-Einstein Manifesto, calling for nuclear disarmament.

Gross, Politzer, Wilczek

Three Americans, David Gross, H. David Politzer and Frank Wilczek shared the 2004 Nobel Prize for Physics. Their elegant mathematical framework describes all physics connected with the strong nuclear force. They have brought physics one step closer to fulfilling a grand dream, to formulate a unified theory – a theory of everything.

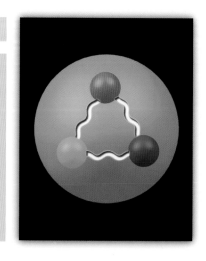

The Sea of Light

Could there be, physicist Paul Dirac asked in 1928, a particle that is identical to the electron in mass but has a positive rather than negative electrical charge? The question was soon answered less than five years later with the discovery in 1932 of cosmic ray collisions.

What if, Dirac continued postulating, that protons, too, had 'antiparticle' equivalents? Indeed, it didn't take researchers long to find that most particles in the universe have 'antimatter' equivalents.

The discovery of antimatter opened the door to what would become an essential addition to the quantum map: Quantum vacuum. In this new unseen world of the nanocosm, even empty space is not truly empty. It's teeming with activity, with virtual particles popping in and out of existence from no where.

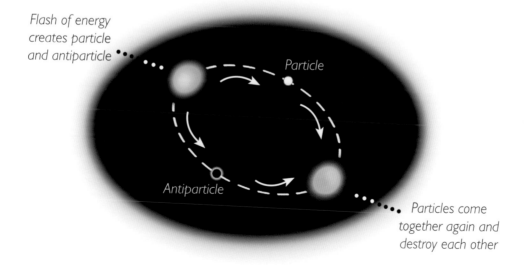

Flash of energy creates particle and antiparticle

Particle

Antiparticle

Particles come together again and destroy each other

A stunning creative subatomic tango perpetually ensues. A particle and its antimatter partner are created out of pure energy. This is called pair creation. In the reverse process, pair annihilation, the particle and antiparticle collide, mutually destruct and disappear forever in a blinding flash of light.

These particles exist for no more than 40 billionth of a second. Talk about a short lifetime! A brief lifetime perhaps, but one of magnificent influence for when collected across the universe, this dance of *Shiva* gives rise to enormous energy. If harnessed, a mere droplet of this energy possesses the potential to power New York City for an entire day. The energy contained in a cubic meter of space could not only heat, but bring to a bubbling boil all the oceans on the planet!

Much like the undulations of the sea or ripples on a pond, the waves on the subatomic level are microscopic oscillations moving through a medium, constantly imprinting a record of the shape of everything. A turbulent 'quantum foam' stretching across the fabric of space-time.

Physicists have searched for the ultimate substance of matter. Little did they realize that the empty space they saw was not empty at all. In quantum reality no vacuum exists. The fundamental substructure of the universe is a glorious sea of light that cannot be eliminated by the laws of physics as we know them today. The apparent 'nothingness' of space hides the secrets of its fundamental building blocks.

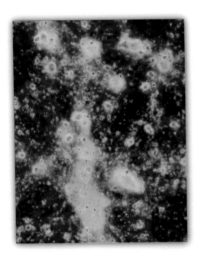

Paul Dirac

Paul Dirac (1902-1984) was not as well known to the public as Einstein, but was nonetheless one of the most influential scientists of the twentieth century. He shared the Nobel Prize in 1933 for the discovery of new and productive forms of atomic theory. He was the successor in the Lucasian chair of mathematics at Cambridge, which was originally Newton's chair.

Quantum Mysticism

Quantum Mysticism

The generous notions about human understanding ... which are illustrated by discoveries in atomic physics are not in the nature of things wholly unfamiliar, wholly unheard of, or new. Even in our own culture they have a history, and in Buddhist and Hindu thought a more considerable and central place. What we shall find is an exemplification, an encouragement, and a refinement of old wisdom.

---Julius Robert Oppenheimer, Science and the Common Understanding

Newton created a worldview of determinism and separateness. He described a 'clockwork' universe that obeyed the laws of motion through time and space. The most separate of these was human consciousness. We sat outside the universe as an observer of events we could not control.

A materialist metaphysical view prevailed in science. Elementary particles formed to make atoms, atoms formed to create molecules, which formed to make cells, including neurons. Neurons formed to make the brain. And the brain created consciousness. This delineation of construction is called upward causation: cause moved up from the micro elementary particles to the macro brain and consciousness. The only causal power in the entities of the world is but the interactions among elementary particles.

But if we are nothing more than material possibilities, how does our observation collapse a wave of possibility? Quantum collapse is a paradox only if upward causation existed in the world.

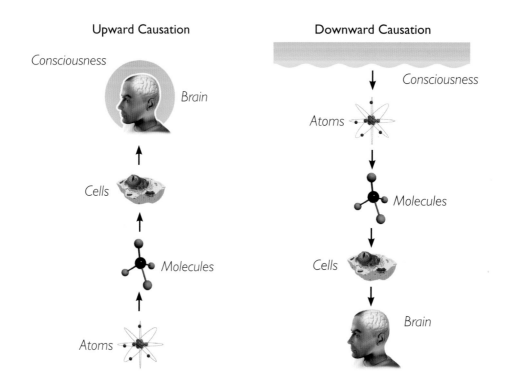

In the correct, paradox-free interpretation, called downward causation, consciousness wields the ultimate power: to create manifest reality by freely choosing among the possibilities offered.

Our consciousness is essential to the process of subatomic particles actualizing, even though it's not included in the mathematics of Bell or Heisenberg. It is *human consciousness* that collapses Schrödinger's cat from a physical dichotomous state into a single one

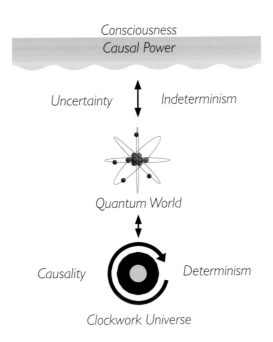

Quantum reality evaporates upon observation. As long as a particle is not observed, measured or interacted within any way, it exists in a curious state that is the superimposition of all possible states. Once the particle is observed, measured or subjected to an interaction the state of superimposition becomes resolved: the particle is then in a single state only, just like an 'ordinary' thing.

An ensemble of energy enfolds both aspects of a particle and a wave. It is the observer's interaction with the ensemble that determines *only* which aspect unfolds and which remains hidden, much in the same way a jeweler manipulates a gemstone to determine which facets become visible and which do not.

When we venture into quantum reality, we cross over into quite an extraordinary domain. It's a dynamic invisible web of interconnection with instant communication between objects, regardless of the distance separating them, violating the speed of light – a domain that transcends both space and time. We enter a 'nonlocal' deeper level of reality in which separateness vanishes and all things are part of an unbroken whole.

At our most fundamental, we are not a chemical reaction, but a 'quantum foam' almost surreal, with an illusory quality. A vast, resonating symphony of wave forms – a 'sea of light', exists out there, transformed into the world we know by our consciousness.

This is nothing more than what the Buddhist and Hindu mystics have been saying for centuries. As Oppenheimer suggests, the concepts of the new physics are neither new nor are they wholly unfamiliar.

As we probe deeper into the quantum world, we find nothing but unexpected glimpses into *Maya*, the illusion. The indeterminate 'quantum reality' becomes meaningful once consciousness is included in the equation. *The universal law of cause and effect, uncertain at the quantum level resurfaces with consciousness as the causal power.*

Consciousness is no longer viewed as brain 'epiphenomena,' but rather as the ground of being, in which all material possibilities, including the brain, is embedded. Animate and inanimate matter, inseparably and intricately interwoven are enfolded throughout the totality of the universe.

Newton plucked life from matter and from us, our consciousness, leaving in its wake a lifelong collection of interlocking parts. Quantum physics, over the past century, dismantled it all and restored consciousness to its rightful place as the causal power of Reality.

Secrets

- Energy, which underlies all nature, is not continuous, but comes in discrete amounts, called quanta.

- A quantum leap is a discontinuous transition between two quantum states.

- Light quanta shows that light is both a wave and a particle.

- All sub-atomic particles demonstrate wave-particle duality.

- A quantum particle can be at more than one place at the same time (the wave property).

- It is not possible to know the exact location of the electron, only its probable location.

- It is impossible at any given moment to measure both the speed and position of an electron.

- Like the side of a coin, the subatomic world reveals only one dimension at a time.

- To observe is to disturb.

- Quantum particles seem to have chameleon-like ability to choose how they want to appear to us.

- Act of observation collapses the coherent superimposition of two waves functions to a single one.

- Quantum universe is 'nonlocal' with instantaneous action-at-a-distance.

- Subatomic particles communicate instantaneously with each other regardless of the distance separating them (faster-than-light communication).

- An atom is made up mostly of space.

- Subatomic particles no longer posses the traits of the matter or objects that they are part of.

- The nucleus makes up more than 99.9% of the atom's mass but only one trillionth of its volume.

- Positively charged particles called protons and neutral particles called neutrons form the nucleus of the atom.

- Negatively charged electrons literally possess no dimension.

- The entire atomic mass of a 70 kg human being is as big as the tip of a needle!

- The subatomic particles can amazingly pass through seemingly impenetrable barriers.

- All matter is composed of two basic groups of particles: leptons and quarks, collectively called fermions.

- The three fundamental forces of the universe are gravity, the strong nuclear force, and the electro-weak force.

- All particles that make up matter have antimatter counterparts.

- Space is not empty. The quantum vacuum is seething with activity.

- The subatomic waves create an interference pattern imprinting a record of the shape of everything.

- Consciousness is not a brain epiphenomena but the ground of being, in which all material possibilities are embedded.

- The subatomic waves are a blueprint of quantum intelligence.

- The interaction of consciousness is essential to the process of subatomic particle actualization.

- The consciousness is ground of everything and exists in all things.

- The concepts in the new physics are not new but have been known for centuries.

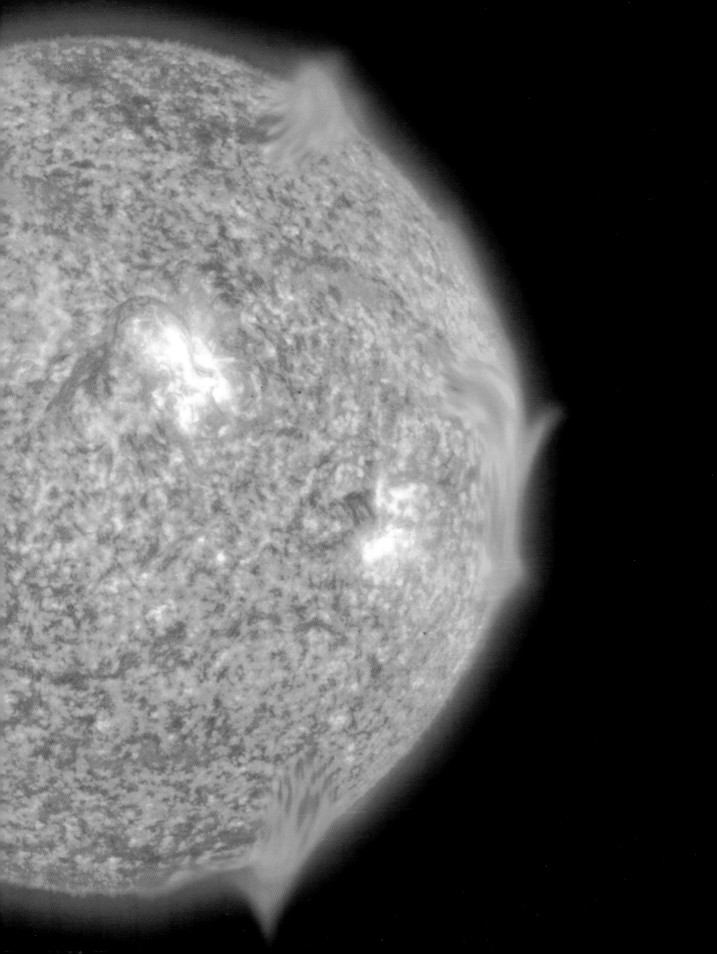

Macrocosm

We find ourselves in a bewildering world. We want to make sense of what we see around us and to ask: What is the nature of the universe?

On any given starry night thousands, perhaps millions, of people crane their necks skyward and allow their minds to swirl around two fundamental questions: Are we alone, and why are we here?

Starting out from the everyday world, we have probed into two directions – outward into the universe at large, and inward into the sub-atomic world.

Fabric of Space-Time

It's All Relative

I was 16 when the image first came to me. What would it be like to ride a beam of light? At 16 I had no idea, but the question stayed with me for the next 10 years. The simple questions are always the hardest. But if I have one gift, it is that I am as stubborn as a mule.

--Albert Einstein

The theory that the Sun is the center of the universe, proposed by Copernicus, revealed the first hint that perhaps the nature of reality depended on the position of the observer. Both Galileo and Newton knew that motion was relative, but insisted that space and time were absolute.

Einstein popped the bubble of the space-time illusion, and with it diffused Nature's absolutes. Things began to change when he intuitively realized his obsession, 'What would it be like to ride a beam of light?'

He found a fundamental 'absolute' frame around which to construct his relative universe: the speed of light. If the speed of light is always the same, regardless of its source, then time is *not* constant, he concluded.

And in doing so, he forever changed our conception of space and time. The lack of an absolute space and time meant we could not determine whether two events that took place at different times occurred in the same position in space.

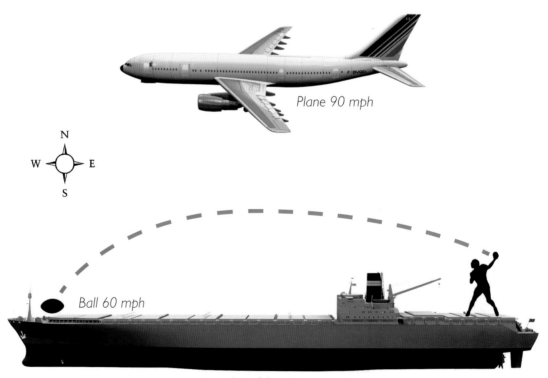

Plane 90 mph

Ball 60 mph

Ship 30 mph

Imagine a football player at the rear of a ship throwing a ball towards the front. The ball's speed is 60 mph. The ship is traveling west at 30 mph. Relative to the ground, then, the speed of the ball is 90 mph.

The football player looks up and sees a small plane flying at the speed of 90 mph – in the same direction of the ship. Relative to the plane, the ball has zero speed – it's not moving. The speed of the football clearly depends on the frame of reference.

In all these measurements, there is the one fixed frame to which the speeds are all relative. But even the earth is not motionless. It's rotating on its axis and revolving in an orbit around the sun. The sun, in turn, is rotating within our galaxy, so it's relative to any other stars … this can go on and on. The fundamental principle of relativity is that all motion is relative.

Einstein recognized that space and time, as well as energy and mass are all relative. He reasoned 'everything is relative' using the speed of light as the reference.

Nicolaus Copernicus

Nicolaus Copernicus (1473-1543) was born in Torun, Poland. He gave a detailed explanation of the heliocentric, or Sun-centered, theory of universe and paved the way to modern astronomy. In fact had it not been for a Protestant Georg Rheticus, a young Professor of Astronomy, Copernicus's masterpiece might never have been published. Copernicus received the printed book on his deathbed. He died of cerebral hemorrhage.

Galileo Galilei

Galileo Galilei (1564-1642) is considered by many to be the founder of the Scientific Revolution. He improvised the newly invented telescope to study the features of celestial bodies and discovered the Moons that circled Jupiter. His application of mathematics to falling bodies became the foundation of classical mechanics and his relativity theory laid the foundation for Einstein's theories of relativity.

The Fourth Dimension

Absolute space, in its own nature, without relation to any thing external, remains always similar and immovable. Absolute, true and mathematical time of itself, and from its own nature, flow equably without relation to anything external.

- Isaac Newton, Principia Mathematica

The relativity of time doesn't really affect us in our daily lives. We move too slowly to be aware of any of its changes. That's why no one ever questioned the Newtonian idea of absolute time. But as we approach the speed of light, things begin to change.

Einstein replaced linear time with relative time. He recognized that time can contract, expand, slow down or speed up depending on the situation of the observer. As passengers in an airplane, for example, we see the runway lights rush past us in a row as the plane taxis before take off. Once we're airborne, however, we view the lights from the vantage point of a higher altitude. The same lights appear closer and closer together until, finally, they're not moving at all.

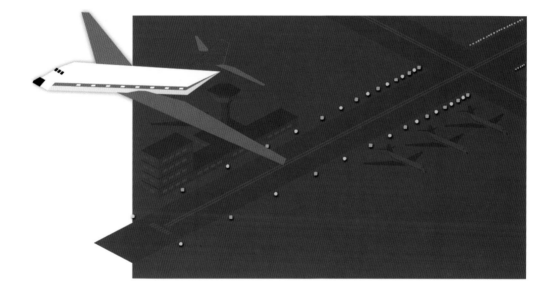

The pattern they follow is the way we experience time. Linear time always appears to be moving, but once we break through the three-dimensional viewpoint, we realize time itself does not move.

As a moving object approaches the speed of light, the time intervals, or the rate at which time passes, change. This is called *time dilation*. Time intervals are the periods of time between events. As the name implies, they dilate – or become longer – as we approach the speed of light.

The speed of an object through space reflects how much of its motion is diverted. The faster something moves through space, the more of its motion is being diverted away from moving through time, so time slows down.

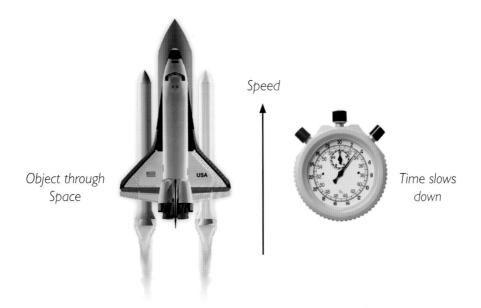

Object through
Space

Speed

Time slows
down

Time continues to slow down the closer the object approaches the speed of light, and by the time it reaches the speed of light it is completely still. Because there is no motion left for time ... the passage of time does not occur at the speed of light. The photons from the big bang are still the same age today as when they first emerged.

The classic explanation of time dilation is the so called twin paradox. One twin travels through space at a velocity approaching the speed of light. The other remains on the planet. Years pass. The twin who traveled through space returns much younger than the one who never left. Yet, it's only a paradox if you believe the idea of absolute time.

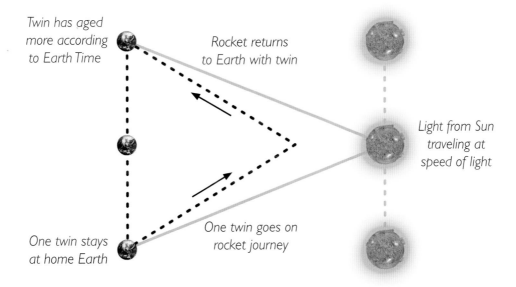

Twin has aged
more according
to Earth Time

Rocket returns
to Earth with twin

Light from Sun
traveling at
speed of light

One twin stays
at home Earth

One twin goes on
rocket journey

From the viewpoint of the earthbound twin, time slowed down for his space-traveling sibling. That's why he appears younger. But from the perspective of the twin in space, time did not slow down. Each sibling processes his own personal measure of time depending on his location and his movement. Relativity is a property of time, not of clocks.

We live and move in an interconnected continuum of space and time. We cannot separate one from the other. We all know what it's like to move through space; we do it all the time. But even if we are sitting still and not moving through space, we're still moving through time. As the old saying goes, 'Time stands still for no man.'

The space-time continuum is composed of four dimensions. Three of these are properties of space: length, width and depth. The fourth is time. Time is a valid and meaningful method of locating any event in our world and universe. Normally, we're aware of moving through space, but we don't often think of time as one of the dimensions in which we operate. We view it more as a commodity or a separate entity. If you want to meet someone for lunch or see a movie, though, it requires that you specify a location in space and a specific location in time.

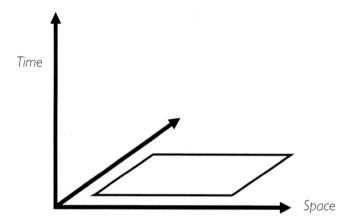

To our senses space and time seem to be two different things. We move around in space that contains three distinct dimensions. We seem to 'move through – or with – time.' And we always move in the same direction, from past to future. We always move at the same speed through time as well: 24 hours per day. We can't go back for a second look at the past. We can't fast forward for a sneak peak at future events. Scientists of the twentieth century discovered that space and time can be described in the same mathematical language, as one entity called space-time. And they labeled time 'the fourth dimension.'

There is one large difference though between time and space. That is our ability to move through it. As noted earlier, we can only travel one way through time. A fixed 'arrow of time' determines our daily activities.

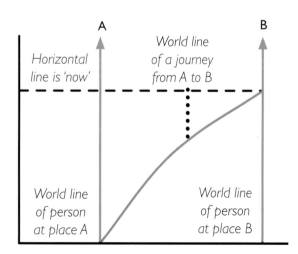

World Lines

Minkowski showed how to represent space-time on paper. 'Upward' is the passage of time, and 'sideways' represents movement through space. A vertical line is someone stationary, and a person who goes on a journey from A to B has a 'world line' that moves through both space and time.

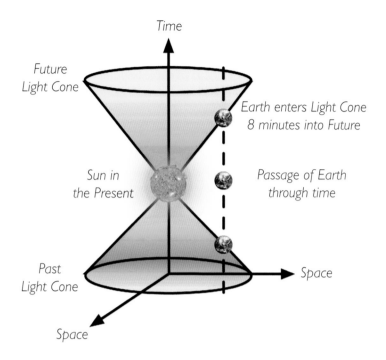

Time

Future
Light Cone

Earth enters Light Cone
8 minutes into Future

Sun in
the Present

Passage of Earth
through time

Past
Light Cone

Space

Space

Sunlight's World Lines

In a Minkowski diagram, light rays are shown as world lines at 45° to the horizontal. The Earth is just over 8 light minutes away from the Sun – it takes light from the Sun 8 minutes to reach the Earth. In this diagram, the Earth moves straight up the page. It does not move in space relative to the Sun. The world line of the Sun's light spreading out forms a three-dimensional cone in a four–dimensional space-time. A beam of light from the Sun travels along the edge of the light cone and only affects the Earth when the Earth has moved 8 and a bit minutes forward in time, to enter the light cone from the beam.

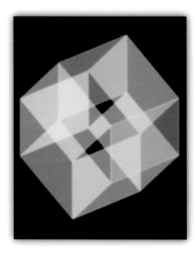

Hermann Minkowski

Hermann Minkowski (1864-1909) was one of Einstein' teachers at the Zurich polytechnic, where Einstein took his degree. A few years later, working at the University of Gottingen, Minkowski explained relativity theory more clearly than Einstein himself had done by introducing the idea of four-dimensional space-time geometry. At the young age of 44, Minkowski died of a ruptured appendix.

It's About Time

Time. Bound by the speed of light and the velocity of nerve impulses, it is first and foremost a form of perception. Nevertheless, we use clocks as our frame of reference for external time. But seconds and minutes are arbitrary, standardized methods of measurement.

Psychological time. It's how we experience time internally. The limits of our ability to perceive time intervals determine how we view the world. If, for example, we could sense the intervals of a duration shorter than 1/24th of a second – which we can't – we would then be able to see the dark gaps between the frames of a movie. If, on the other end of the spectrum, we could perceive much longer intervals of time, then we could actually watch children grow.

We travel constantly between two parallel universes of external and internal time. We can acquire an understanding of time by focusing on the relation between time and the physical world and the relation between time and consciousness.

The smallest movement of time that consciousness can grasp is the microcosmic I-time. This is the time it takes to think the sound of a short vowel – not a consonant, since a consonant cannot be uttered without a vowel! The psychic measure or value, therefore, is a single syllabic unit of vibration.

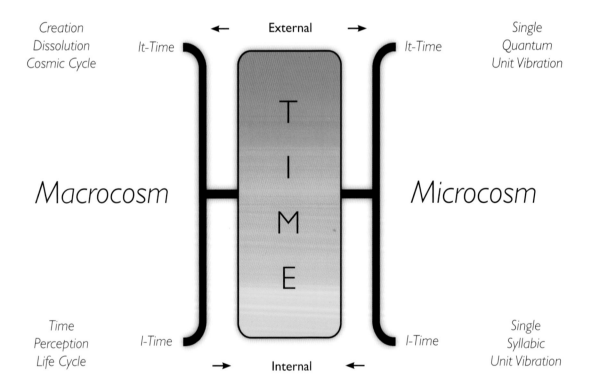

Our concept of I-time and space, of being small or large, at the macrocosmic level, changes as we age. The interval from one birthday to another, for a child, is an 'eternity'. The passing of a year simply vanishes as we grow in consciousness. That which we once considered a long space of time now seems quite short the older you get.

We measure objective time as cosmological time. It seems to travel and stretch from the smallest nanosecond of an atomic clock to the eons of history, unfolding and disappearing.

The microscopic It-time, the finest vibration of a single quantum, is the measurement of how long it takes an electron to 'orbit' the nucleus of an atom. At the microscopic level, this is most commonly calculated in nanoseconds, one of which is one-billionth of a second!

The world of subatomic particles expresses extremely short, precise time intervals. Lest you think that employing this time is an exercise in futility, consider this: this time measurement is most useful on board atomic clocks in Global Positioning Systems (GPS) satellites. A time error of a millionth of a second from a single satellite can distort a GPS receiver by as much as a fifth of a mile.

From nanoseconds to light years, time gets lost in the dimension of macroscopic It-time. Our closest star, Proxima Centaura, is four light years – or 24,000,000,000,000 (24 trillion) miles away. This confounds our imagination.

An instant can be 10 million years in cosmological time. Those 10 million years represent only 1/450 of the Earth's history thus far. We find this difficult to comprehend because we are so accustomed to thinking that a year is one of the natural divisions of time.

It is easy to forget that the time interval we know as a year is nothing more than one revolution of the earth around the Sun. Similarly, the planet Mercury takes a longer time to revolve on its axis than to rotate once around the Sun. Talk about a confusing birthday party!

The Arrow of Time

For the majority of us, time is not only very real, it's the master of all we do. We are—either by nature or through training – clock watchers. Mystified by its nature—an apparent oddity separated into past, present and future – the human mind is without a doubt preoccupied with time.

We view time as a continuum where one event flows into another from the past to the future. Our memory and objectivity of the impermanence of all things governs our subjective sense of the directional nature of time.

What, then, denotes the difference between the past and the future? Why do we remember the past, but cannot recall the future? Increasing disorder, or what scientists call entropy, distinguishes the past from the future, giving time a direction. The classic example of entropy is a car rusting in a junk yard. Entropy disintegrates the orderly machinery into crumbling dust.

Similarly, the nursery rhyme about Humpty Dumpty gives us another illustration of entropy. You'll recall that 'Humpty Dumpty sat on the wall. Humpty Dumpty had a great fall. All the king's horses and all the king's men couldn't put Humpty back together again.' He was broken irretrievably into pieces, clearly in a more disorderly state than at the beginning of the rhyme. We measure time in the direction in which disorder increases.

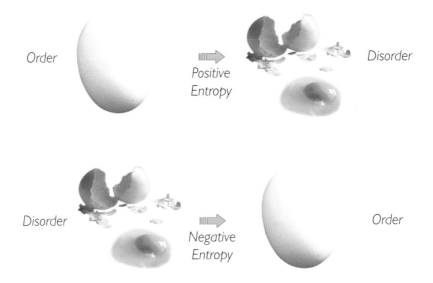

Order   Positive   Disorder
               Entropy

Disorder   Negative   Order
               Entropy

It's no coincidence that the brain's synapses fire in a linear fashion – and that we view time in a linear direction. Research now proves that our experience of time is directly related to how the brain works physiologically. We experience time as a linear event because our brain processes information in a linear manner.

It is the direction in which we feel the passage of time, the direction in which we remember the past, but not the future. When we dream, however, this directional nature grows indistinct and mysteriously disappears as we fall into a deep sleep. Past. Present. Future. All flow into the other. The separation is lost when we sleep. President Abraham Lincoln dreamed about his own assassination a week before he died.

This 'arrow of time' is, perhaps, a necessary evil for our physical bodies to operate in the waking state. What humans consume for survival is ordered energy. Our bodies convert it to heat, which is a disordered form of energy. Our definition of linear time is really an illusion of how we perceive change.

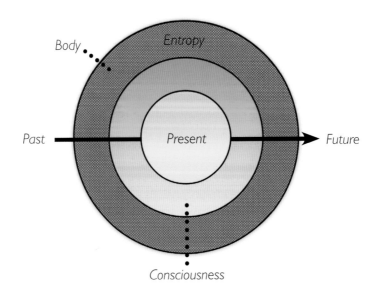

The most tangible evidence of the progression of time is our own aging. We sense that we exist in time because our own body is continually undergoing change. In Sanskrit the word for the human body is *deha*, which literally means decay or entropy.

Entropy, though, doesn't apply to consciousness, the unseen part of us immune to the ravages of time. Eastern philosophers have always argued this. The very notion of the passage of time, they said, is nonsense. The idea of the river or the flux of time is founded on a misconception. Time only appears to be an intrinsic form of existence: to exist is to be inserted in duration, forever transforming the future into the past through an ungraspable present. In reality, everything, is in the eternal present.

'The very idea of space-time is a wrong idea,' John Wheeler, an eminent physicist wrote, 'and with that idea failing, the idea of 'before' and 'after' also fails. That can be said so simply and yet it is so hard for the lesson to grab hold in the world.'

Several western philosophers suspected as much. Among them, St. Augustine, believed that time was nothing more than a subjective experience we project out onto the world. It had no meaning or reality, he said, outside of us.

Time does not exist as an absolute, nor does it flow, as it is marked off by the resonance of atoms or events viewed in linear sequence.

The person who meditates replaces the Newtonian idea of an absolute time and space and Einstein's view of a relative space-time with a reality that comes far closer to the truth. The universe exists as one vast 'here and now' where here represents all points in space. 'Now' represents time in a single instant. *Time is quantified eternity; Space is quantified infinity.*

We spend almost all our time thinking about the past or future – with very little thought spent on the present moment. Seldom do we sit doing nothing while contemplating the present moment – probably because we don't have the time!

Where there is no time, then all we have is the present moment. That moment lasts indefinitely. We experience time even in the moment, as the movement of one moment to the next: *now* and *now* and *now*.

As we approach the speed of *light*, the intervals between moments become slower and slower, until all of a sudden we are in the present moment forever. The idea of time stopping is infinity and eternity, is called en*light*enment.

The Most Famous Equation

Space and time were relative. The only constant left in the universe was the speed of light. Or so we thought.

Einstein's famous equation extended the concept of relatively to include both energy and matter. $E=mc^2$ revealed the interrelationship between these two quantities.

The conversion of matter into energy occurs every single day. Every time we light a fire we transform the energy of matter into the energy of heat. Einstein demonstrated this conversion by using the radioactive decay of the element radium.

Radium emits an alpha particle, leaving the element polonium. However, the masses of the alpha particle and the polonium do not equal what remains in the radium. Mass had been lost! Einstein knew the total energy released, E, in his equation, as well as the missing mass, m and developed the equation:

$$E=mc^2$$

The mass of a body reflects its energy content. Basically two sides of the same coin, this pair is sometimes referred to as a mass-energy equivalence. The speed of light, c, ties energy and mass together. When squared, the resulting number is enormous. Therefore the energy in a minute amount of mass is huge. A kilogram of anything holds enough energy to boil a hundred billion kettles. Or destroy a city.

Einstein's theory, though, also explains why mass increases as it approaches the speed of light. The conversion of energy into mass is not as familiar to us as the conversion of mass into energy, but it happens just as often, nonetheless. The faster an object moves, the more mass it gains. Just as mass has energy, energy similarly possesses mass. Four and half pounds of sunlight hit the earth every second!

Mass vs. Weight

There's an interesting distinction that should be made regarding weight and mass. While weight is defined by the force of gravity acting on an object and is equal to the mass of the object times the acceleration of gravity, it can vary in different gravitational fields. We weigh less on the Moon than on Earth.

Mass, on the other hand, measures the amount of matter an object contains and is unaffected by gravity. The only way to increase an object's mass is to add atoms.

It's Still Relative

Sitting in a chair in the Patent Office at Berne (in 1907), a sudden thought occurred to me. 'If a person falls he will not feel his own weight.' I was startled and this simple thought made a deep impression on me. It impelled me towards a theory of gravitation. It was the happiest thought of my life.

– Albert Einstein

Maxwell married electricity and magnetism in the 1800s and named it electro-magnetism. Einstein, with his famous equation, wed mass and energy. His theory of special relativity resulted in the union of space and time. Only one force was left to complete the puzzle: gravity.

Having already sidestepped absolute space and time, Einstein's took the universe and twisted it into fantastic new shapes. General relativity was an extension of his special theory that also included the effects of the force of gravity.

Einstein knew that a freefall cancels the effect of gravitation. Galileo had discovered that all objects fall at the same rate, regardless of their mass. But without a frame of reference it's impossible to differentiate between the force of acceleration and that of gravity. Here was Einstein's happiest thought!

Einstein's theory encompasses two aspects. To explain the first part, we'll use the example of a person traveling in a spaceship. He possesses no experimental or intuitive means to distinguish whether he is motionless on the surface of the earth or if he is in space accelerating at a rate equivalent to 1G – or earth gravity.

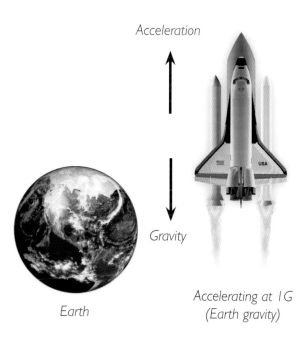

Acceleration

Gravity

Earth

Accelerating at 1G
(Earth gravity)

This implies, Einstein postulated, that the acceleration due to motion and that due to gravity are equivalent. This is the principle of equivalence.

The second aspect of general relativity is based on the exotic notion of a space-time that is curved. The force of gravity is the unseen geometry of space. If this is difficult to visualize, think of a rubber sheet with a heavy object like a bowling ball on it. The mass of the ball depresses or warps the rubber. If a smaller object, like a marble, is rolled onto the sheet, the marble would fall into the curved path of the depression the bowling ball created. If the marble has just the right speed and direction, it would fly into orbit around the ball.

We think of space as being empty; but it's really more like an invisible, stretched sheet of rubber. A lump of matter in space – like the Sun – makes a dent in space-time, like a bowling ball sitting on a trampoline. Anything falling past this lump of matter must follow a curved path, or the line of least resistance, called a geodesic. In other words, matter tells space-time how to bend. Space-time tells matter how to move.

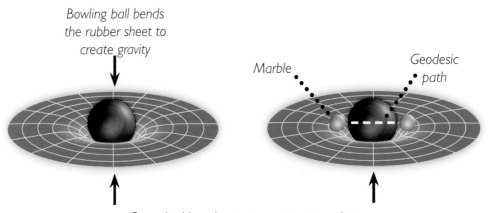

Bowling ball bends the rubber sheet to create gravity

Marble

Geodesic path

Curved rubber sheet represents space-time

The general theory of relativity is a theory of gravity, then. Its effects can only be explained when there are strong gravitational fields at work that is when there are large masses distorting space-time. When gravity is weak, there are minuscule differences between Einstein's predictions and those of Newton's theory of gravity. Newton's theory works well enough for us in our daily lives.

But there are far more shocking predictions. When matter is squeezed very tightly, space is stretched to breaking point. An infinitely deep well appears in the space-time continuum, and gravity becomes so strong that nothing can escape. This is a black hole. Astronomers now believe that the universe is littered with these monsters and that a giant hole is sitting in the center of our own galaxy.

Gravity Bends Light!

If matter follows the curve of geodesics in space-time, then it follows that light rays are bound to do the same. The fact that space is curved means light does not travel in a straight line throughout space. So, general relativity predicts that gravity bends light.

The theory anticipates, for example, that light from a distant star passing near the Sun would be deflected through a small angle. This would cause the star to appear in a different position to an observer on Earth. Normally, this effect would be difficult to see since the Sun's brightness makes it impossible to observe starts appearing near the Sun. This effect would be visible only during a lunar eclipse of the Sun.

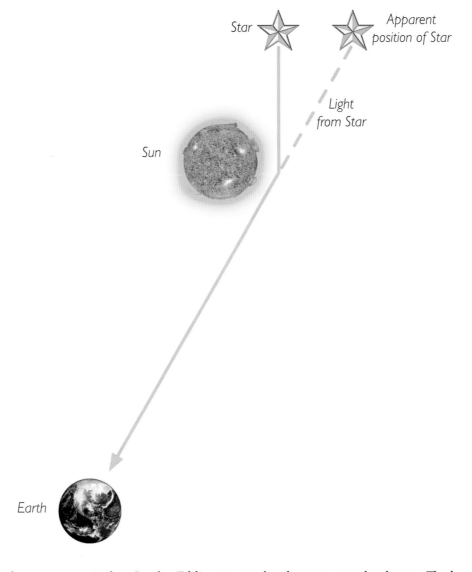

In 1919, British astronomer, Arthur Stanley Eddington got the chance to test the theory. The lunar eclipse of May 29 of that year provided optimal conditions for such an experiment. He led an expedition to the island of Principe off the coast of West Africa to photograph the eclipse.

He discovered that light rays, which left the surface of stars thousands of years ago, had been bent by curved space close to the Sun only eight minutes previously. The rays passed through the lens and exposed the photographic plates at the moment Einstein had postulated. One of the most remarkable experiments in scientific history had been completed. Since then, light deflection has been confirmed with amazing accuracy by numerous observations.

Sir Arthur Eddington

Sir Arthur Eddington (1882-1944) was one of the most prominent astrophysicists of his time. He helped to confirm some of Einstein's work and was one of the earliest creators of the concept of relativity. He spent a great amount of time researching the internal makeup of stars. The finding of a star's maximum luminosity is now called the Eddington limit.

Elegant
Universe

Afterglow of Creation

For most of us, it's hard to imagine Einstein making a mistake. But following the introduction of General Relativity, this physicist tried to apply the new gravitational dynamics to the universe as a whole. He eventually admitted this to be 'the biggest blunder' of his life! He put forth a cosmological view of a homogeneous finite universe, one residing in a four-dimensional sphere, curved by the forces of gravity, as predicted in his theory of relativity.

By 1929, however, sufficient evidence existed to support the fact that the universe was not at all homogenous. Instead, it was clumpy and expanding. Edwin Hubble, most widely known today because a telescope and a space mission are named for him, observed that the galaxies were moving away from each other. He based this on the degree of red-shift he had observed.

As a galaxy or even a star travels away from us, its light shifts to the red end of the spectrum. This phenomenon is comparable to a train whistle's pitch dropping as it moves past you. The red-shift indicates the light source is traveling away from us at a high velocity. This discovery overturned the long-held belief that the universe was static and finite.

Astrophysicist George-Henri Lemaitre studied Hubble's observations. If the universe were finite in both time and space, he suggested, and if it were expanding outward, then it must have begun from a point of non-expansion. This single point in time and space is called a singularity. Lemaitre labeled the point the 'primeval atom.' Thus the theory of the spontaneous explosion model of the universe was born.

This theory proved controversial, to say the least. British astronomer Fred Hoyle dismissed it outright. 'Every cluster of galaxies, every star, every atom had a beginning,' Hoyle asserted, 'but the universe itself did not.' He derisively labeled the theory 'The Big Bang.' Ironically, the term would be commonly used.

The explosions of the atomic bombs in World War II prompted George Gamow to draw an analogy to the Big Bang. Gamow theorized that nuclear reactions generated during the creation of the universe would produce all light chemical elements, such as hydrogen and helium. Later, as the universe continued to cool heavier atoms would started to form. Matter would eventually reorganize itself into stars and galaxies.

As cogent as this argument seemed, the most important piece of evidence was yet to appear. In 1965, two researchers at Bell Labs in New Jersy, Arno Penzias and Robert Wilson, verified cosmic microwave background radiation. And just what is this? It's best described as the diluted afterglow of the titanic explosion of the Big Bang. This stunning confirmation of the predicted radiation convinced scientists that the Big Bang was indeed 'the answer' to the origin of the universe.

Perhaps, it is easiest to visualize the Big Bang, which occurred 12 to 15 billion years ago, by imagining a movie of the universe being played backwards in time. A given spherical region of the universe shrinks, slowly at first, but more rapidly as the radius of the sphere reaches zero. It is here, at this juncture, that all the matter and energy that had been contained in that volume of space is now compressed into a single point, or singularity. In this idealized model, the entire observable universe is considered to have started out compressed into one single point.

The fundamental features of the universe – space, time, and matter – were hidden, embedded inside this singularity. There could be no 'outside', nor did there exist a dimensional space for it to explode into. The Big Bang created time-space itself, a concept that defies the boundaries of our logic.

As popular as this theory is, it can't account for some lingering questions. An alternative theory to the creation of the universe is The Steady State Theory of Plasma Cosmology. While the name may be intimidating, its concept is really not all that difficult. This approach denies the universe began from nothing, somewhere in time. Instead, it says we see an evolving universe that is constantly changing. This universe has always existed and has always evolved and will continue to do so for eternity.

Unlike the theory underlying the Big Bang, plasma cosmology sees the universe formed and controlled by the electromagnetic interaction of matter and anti-matter, not just gravitation. The steady state theory accounts for the 'clumpiness' and the fluctuations in the microwave background radiation.

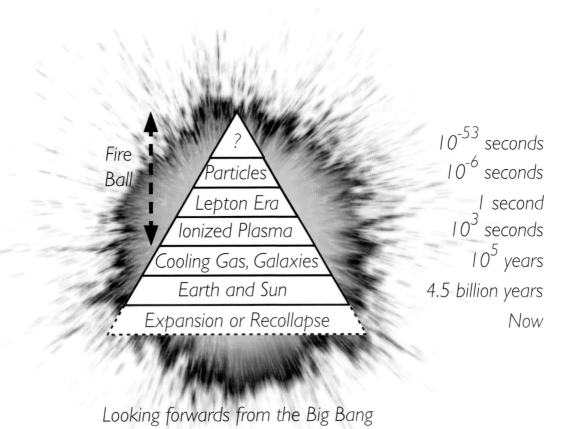

Fire
Ball

?	10^{-53} seconds
Particles	10^{-6} seconds
Lepton Era	1 second
Ionized Plasma	10^3 seconds
Cooling Gas, Galaxies	10^5 years
Earth and Sun	4.5 billion years
Expansion or Recollapse	Now

Looking forwards from the Big Bang

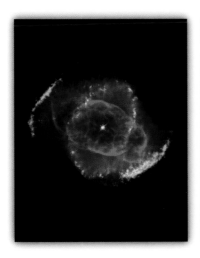

Edwin Hubble

Edwin Hubble (1889-1953) was a man who changed our view of the universe. Watching the heavens from Mt. Wilson in southern California, he showed that galaxies are moving away from us with a speed proportional to their distance. Hubble was also remarkable for his athletic ability, breaking the Illinois State high jump record and won a Rhodes scholarship to Oxford where he studied law. He returned to US and decided that his future lay in astronomy.

George-Henri Lemaitre

George-Henri Lemaitre (1894-1966) combined two vocations not very often associated: astrophysics with Catholic priesthood. Born in Belgium, he represents a synthesis of the paradigm of science and religion into a layered perspective. He is credited with proposing the Big Bang Theory of the origin of the universe, although he called his 'hypothesis of the primeval atom.'

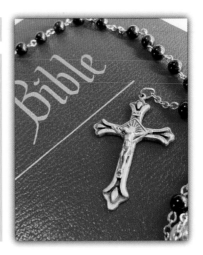

Sir Fred Hoyle

Sir Fred Hoyle (1915-2001) was a distinguished and controversial British astronomer, mathematician, and novelist, who rejected what became popularly known as the Big Bang Theory. It was Hoyle, in fact, that coined the term as a sarcastic rebuke to its proposal. 'Every cluster of galaxies, every star, every atom had a beginning, but the universe itself did not,' Hoyle claimed.

George Gamow

George Gamow, a Russian-born scientist working on the Manhattan Project, popularized his theory of the Big Bang as fact in the last chapter of his book, 'One, Two, Three, Infinity.' He became interested in astronomy by examining the starry sky through a little telescope, his father's present on the thirteenth birthday of his son.

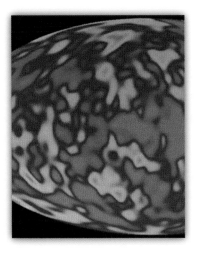

Arno Penzias & Robert Wilson

Arno Penzias and Robert Wilson were awarded the 1978 Nobel Prize for physics for their invaluable discovery of microwave cosmic background. First they found 'a white dielectric substance' (i.e. pigeon droppings) in their detector, and checked for other possible malfunctions, but soon ruled these out. The noise detected was the radiation and was interpreted as an echo of the Big Bang.

Big Bang

To begin at the beginning: an explosion occurred. In that very first instant, which lasted approximately one-trillionth of a second, the subatomic universe grew to the size of a soccer ball. It was, at this time, a seething, boiling cauldron in which energy transformed into matter and conversely matter transformed into energy.

This radiation energy was converted into matter that took the form of subatomic pairs of particles and antiparticles. These annihilated each other to change back into radiation. Not all particles, though, were annihilated. There were slightly more particles than antiparticles – about one billion and one particles for every billion antiparticles. This, indeed, would have huge consequences later in the formation of the universe.

As the universe grew, it became a cooler and much quieter place. Those one in a billion particles with no antimatter equivalents with which to mutually destruct were stranded. They became the first stable subatomic particles – the building blocks of the atoms: protons, neutrons and electrons.

Three minutes into the Big Bang, as the temperature cooled to slightly above one billion degrees; a portion of the protons and neutrons that collided fused to form the heart of atoms – the atomic nuclei. Hydrogen, helium, and lithium were the first nuclei created. Just as quickly as it had begun, the Big Bang had ended!

The Unseen Universe

Nearly 99 percent of the universe is made of unseen dark matter. What we do see – the stars, galaxies and literally everything else – constitutes only about one percent of total matter in the universe. The hidden matter, though, is undetectable, for it does not emit any form of electromagnetic radiation. It is revealed through its gravitational influence on visible matter, such as the stars and galaxies.

End of the Universe

We've discussed two possible theories on the origin of the universe. But how do scientists believe it will end … or will it ever end?

Current thought provides three possible options. The first is that the universe will simply continue expanding forever; the second option proposes that at some future point it will stop expanding, start contracting, and eventually collapse. Finally, the third possible scenario is that neither of the other two will occur. The universe will continue to expand and contract forever. Which of these actually will take place depends on only one thing: the total gravity of all matter in the universe.

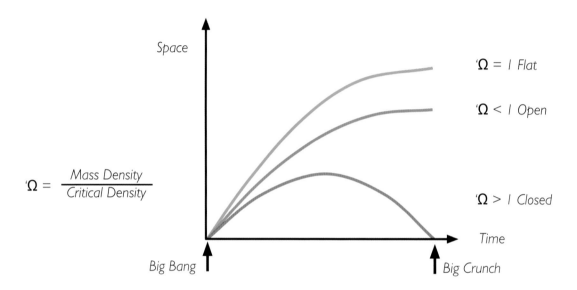

The gravitational energy of an object is directly proportionate to its mass density: the higher the mass density, the greater the gravitational energy. A neutron star, with its compact nature, has a mass similar to the Sun, but its radius is seventy thousand times smaller. Consequently, gravity near the surface of the neutron star is about five billion times stronger than that near the surface of the Sun.

Critical density is the name for the value, which separates eternal expansion from eventual contraction. It's denoted by using appropriately enough, the last letter of the Greek alphabet, Omega.

If the density of the universe is higher than the critical density, then gravity prevails. Expansion will stop and contraction will occur. Scientists denote this as Omega > 1. This indicates a 'closed' universe, one which could collapse back to a single point, in effect replicating the Big Bang in reverse. This scenario is often called the Big Crunch, where the end point of infinite density, called the Omega Point, is reached.

If the mass density is lower than the critical density, then the universe will continue to expand forever. (Omega<1) Cosmologists refer to this as an 'open' universe; it will expand forever because there is not enough matter to stop it.

The third alternative is a 'flat' universe. This is where the mass density equals the gravitational force. Expansion will continue forever, as in the open universe model, but the speed at which it extends approaches zero as time progresses (Omega=1).

Even if the universe lasts forever, its contents – the planets and the stars – were born and eventually die. The raw materials of the universe will slowly die out, until one day the last star will die and with that matter will cease to exist. Space-time itself will continue, but there will be no matter left in it. This should not be an issue for us to worry about, because as far as scientists can tell, nothing this drastic will happen to our cosmos for a very, very long time.

The Search for Unity

As far as the laws of mathematics refer to reality, they are not certain, and as far as they are certain, they do not refer to reality.

-- *Albert Einstein*

The ultimate Theory of Everything. This is the Holy Grail of Physics: to discover the all-powerful theory from which every naturally occurring phenomenon in the entire universe could be explained.

If you reach back far enough in the history of the universe, you'll discover that the four fundamental forces, along with the particles carrying these forces, came from what physicists call a 'singularity.' By the time the universe was three minutes old, however, these forces were already distinctly separate and the basic building blocks of helium and hydrogen, the two elements that compose 99 percent of all visible matter were present.

Twentieth century physicists see their goal to not only find and classify all fundamental particles, but to understand the way these particles interact with each other and to reveal the origin of the forces among them.

Most phenomena we see around us require no more than a combination of Newton's laws of mechanics and Maxwell's electromagnetic theory. At either end of this scale lie the two extreme worlds of the very small or nanocosm, described by quantum mechanics, and the very large or macrocosm, described by general relativity.

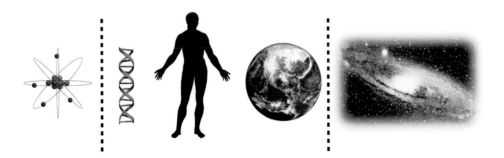

The search for the Theory of Everything is called 'the unification of physics.' Einstein thought it more appropriate to call it 'reading the mind of God.' He spent most of his later years searching for a unified theory. The universe, though, was not ready to reveal its secrets. Partial theories for gravity and electro-magnetism existed, but little was known about nuclear forces.

Sheldon Glashow eventually pried the secrets from nature when he showed that the two forces, nuclear weak and the electromagnetic, were really different aspects of the same entity, now called the 'electro-weak force.' The weak, strong, and electromagnetic forces can be combined into the so-called 'grand unified theory,' or GUT. However, this theory does not account for the presence of gravity.

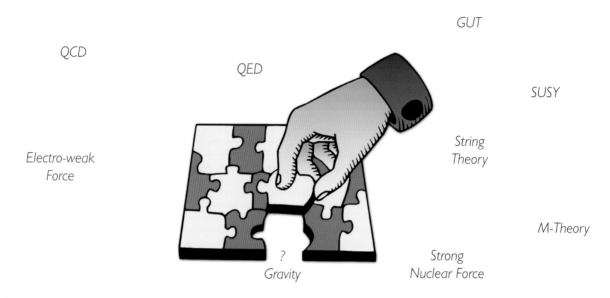

Physicists believe that right after the Big Bang, all the forces of nature were identical and all the elementary particles were the same. Within an instant, this symmetry though broke down, as the universe cooled and expanded, eventually producing these distinctive identities.

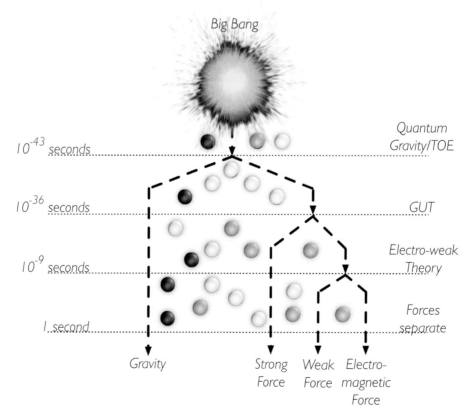

A great example of 'symmetry breaking' is water and its changing forms. Water looks the same despite the angle from which you view it. But it also becomes more complex as it changes form into a snowflake. The crystalline flake looks the same in only six directions. Whenever a structure becomes more complex, symmetry, or at least the original symmetry, is lost.

Similarly, a ball on top of the 'Mexican hat' represents an unstable symmetry that is broken when it rolls off in any direction. This is the breakdown of symmetry scientists are trying to understand in reverse. This is the cornerstone concept from which the theory of super symmetry or SUSY was born.

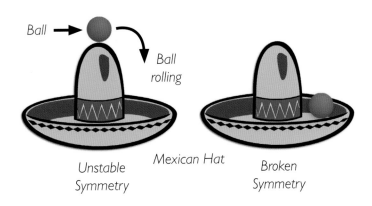

Ball

Ball rolling

Unstable Symmetry

Mexican Hat

Broken Symmetry

The merger of special relativity and electro-magnetism represents the first attempt at unifying relativity and quantum mechanics. This created the theory of quantum electrodynamics, or QED. Paul Dirac established the roots of QED in the 1930s. He theorized that the interaction between charged particles could be described in terms of photons being exchanged between particles. An electron swapping a single photon with another electron was the simplest process possible. Richard Feynman later described this with great precision.

These discoveries led to another set of theories that merged the strong and weak forces. Called quantum chromodynamics, or QCD, it describes the ways quarks interact with one another. Quarks come in three 'colors': red, blue and green. The 'chromo' in the theory's name originates from the way the 'color' of the quark changes when it interacts with the gluons.

Physicists realize now that in order to unify the four forces of nature, they must find a way of combining general relativity with the quantum field theory. Science has advanced in the understanding of quantum mechanics, physicists argue, but gravity should also be able to be described in these terms.

One such theory is in the developing stages. It's called the String Theory and attempts to explain gravity through an exchange particle called the graviton. The String Theory, though, as its name suggests, differs in a remarkable way from earlier quantum field theories. At the very heart of the atom, the hypothesis proposes, the smallest particles are, in fact, tiny, vibrating loops called strings. The resonating vibratory patterns differ for each individual string and basically define the particle, much in the same way our fingerprints define our identities.

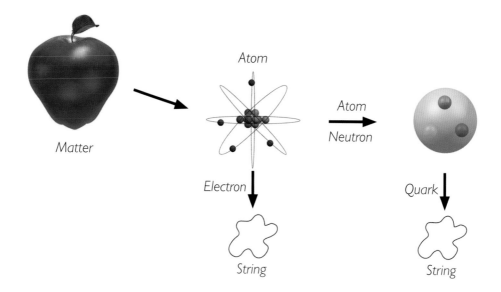

Individually, each particular particle creates its own separate 'music.' Cosmically, entire stars and galaxies – all composed at their very core of these tiny strings – vibrate together. In fact, every element of the universe vibrates harmoniously together, creating a cosmic symphony. This theory could actually decode the most fundamental harmonies.

The vibrating strings, used to explain the behavior of quarks and other particles, come in two varieties. If they have ends, they are called 'open strings.' If they are joined with themselves in closed loops, they are called 'closed strings.' Other properties of the strings – such as their charge – are 'tied' to the end of the string.

An open string moves through space-time, tracing a 'world sheet' instead of a world line. A loop of string traces out a tube. Strings can collide and connect and then just as easily separate again.

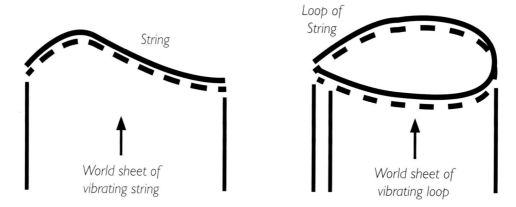

When two strings collide, they may join at their ends to make a third type of string, which splits apart to make two new strings. If two loops combine to form a single one, they sweep out the world line of space-time 'trousers.' Similarly, a single string can divide into two.

Scientists hope the String Theory will help to further the development of a Theory of Everything, that eventually not only explains all four forces, but also the structure of space-time. Nature, perhaps, will release these secrets slowly, over the coming decades.

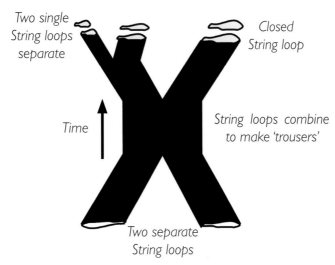

Two single
String loops
separate

Closed
String loop

Time

String loops combine
to make 'trousers'

Two separate
String loops

Even if a single mathematical equation is found that accounts for all the laws and constants of physical nature, it is unlikely to embrace all the diverse phenomenon of the world. For only when the nanocosm is united with the macrocosm, will the most complete picture of the structure of the universe be unveiled. Until then, the search for unity remains an ambition and a hope.

Richard Feynman

Richard Feynman (1918-1988), the greatest physicist of his generation, was one of the founders of quantum electrodynamics. He received the Nobel Prize in 1965 and was a key member of the panel that investigated the 1986 Challenger disaster.

Sheldon Glashow

Sheldon Glashow (b.1932) was an American theoretical physicist who, with Steven Weinberg and Abdus Salam, received the Nobel Prize for Physics in 1979 for formulating the electroweak theory.

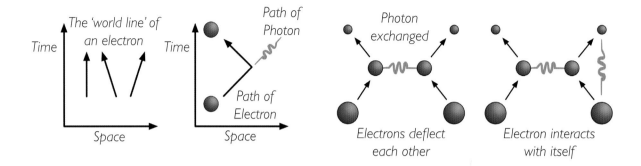

The 'world line' of an electron

Time

Space

Path of Photon

Path of Electron

Time

Space

Photon exchanged

Electrons deflect each other

Electron interacts with itself

Quantum Electrodynamics – QED

This is the theory concerning the interaction of light with matter and is the most fundamental and the most important proposition in the whole of science.

With the exception of gravity and the forces within the nucleus of the atom, QED explains all processes in nature. It clarifies such diverse activity as how hydrogen and oxygen atoms combine to make a water molecule, the nature of sunlight as well as how the electrical signals from the brain are converted to reflexes.

Best understood through the use of Feynman's diagrams, this theory visually shows the paths of electrons called 'world lines.' Placed within two coordinates of time and space, a vertical line indicates a stationary electron whose position is not changing. By contrast, an angled 'world line' represents change. The incline of the slope predicts not only its changing position in space, but also the speed of the electron. The greater the slope, the greater is the rate of change as well as the faster its speed.

A photon associated with the field of a magnet can be introduced into the diagram. It is shown interacting with an electron traveling in a straight line and then deflecting it onto a new path. A moving electron emits or absorbs a photon, causing its direction to change. This straightforward version of QED predicts that a property, called the magnetic movement of the electron, has a value of exactly one (1). The experiments show that magnetic movement is actually a little more than one.

Feynman illustrated this interaction through mathematical calculations to an accuracy of 0.00000001 percent. This, by the way, is the most precise agreement between theory and observation for any experiment ever carried out.

Holographic Universe

Holograms are a revolutionary way of viewing a unified theory of everything. A hologram is produced when a single laser beam is split into two separate beams. One, called, the 'working beam,' is reflected off an object to be imaged, in this instance, an apple. The other laser, called the 'reference beam' reflects the image unaltered on a photographic plate. The two beams crisscross each other, producing an interference pattern of stripes and whorls on the plate.

To the naked eye, the holographic figure recorded on the film is a meaningless whorl, like the ripples on a pond when a handful of pebbles are tossed into it. But when another laser beam is shone on the plate, a three-dimensional representation of the original object appears.

The three-dimensional quality of the image is very convincing, much like that of Princess Leia shining out of R2D2 in the popular movie Star Wars. We can view this holographic image of the apple from different angles. However, if we tried to touch the image, our hand would pass right through it. Like an apparition, there is no physical matter to hold, because the hologram is an energy interference pattern: an intangible, magnified image of the apple. The hologram is not the object itself.

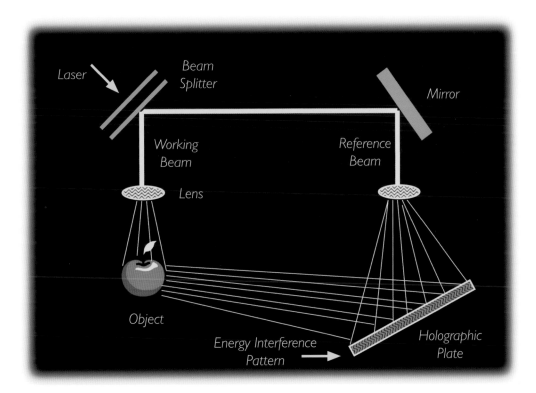

The three-dimensional quality of the image is not the only remarkable aspect of this figure. Every piece that composes this pattern contains the entire image of the object intact. Even if the holographic film were cut into a million pieces when illuminated by a laser, each piece would still, amazingly, reveal its own miniature apple!

The intangible quality of this feature excited David Bohm. It proved to be a metaphor for understanding undivided wholeness. Its explanatory power seemed custom tailored for his purpose. A wide range of phenomena that previously had been deemed as lying outside the providence of scientific understanding now made sense.

The longer Bohm contemplated it, the more he came to realize the universe employed holographic principles. He crystallized the concept in his book *Wholeness and the Implicate Order*. He viewed the universe as a giant hologram.

Just as holographic film gives birth to the hologram, our reality is buttressed by a deeper order of existence, a vast primary level of reality that gives birth to all the objects and their appearances. This is called the 'implicate' or enfolded order, while the level of our existence is the 'explicate' or unfolded order.

All manifestation, then, is the result of countless enfoldings and unfoldings, a multiplexing of many overlapping holograms. Each carries information of a slightly different nature of the universe. The universe, however, is not a static hologram, but rather a 'holomovement.'

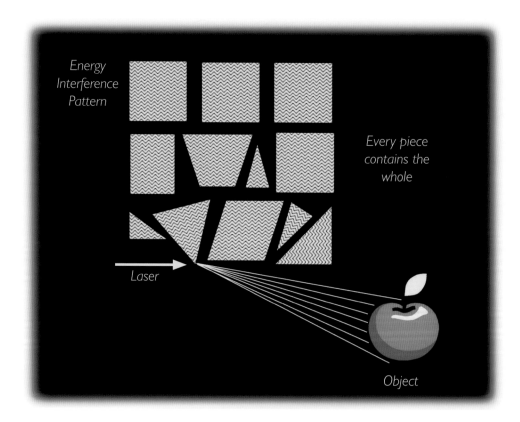

Despite the appearance of the separate nature of matter, at the explicate level, everything is in fact, grounded in an implicate order of reality. This undeveloped wholeness means that all that is in the universe is actually a part of a continuum.

We are not just composed of the same things – *we are the same thing*. One enormous reality unfolds itself into uncountable atoms, bubbling oceans, twinkling stars and swirling galaxies in the cosmos. An unbroken whole, it is virtually impossible to determine where any given whirlpool ends and the river begins.

The implicate order is the fundamental ground of everything in the universe, from every subatomic particle that has ever been or will be, to every configuration of matter, energy, life, and consciousness that is possible, to the double helix of the DNA to the Andromeda Galaxy.

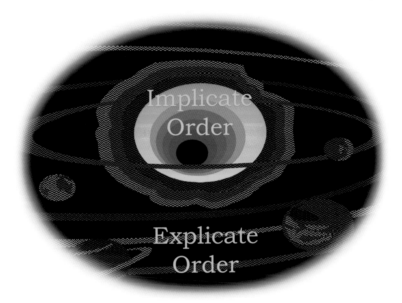

Animate and inanimate matter is inseparably intertwined. Life itself is enfolded throughout the entire universe. Even a rock, therefore, is in some way alive, for life and intelligence is present not only in all of physical matter, but life is present in energy, space, and time. Intelligence underlies the fabric of the universe. The past, the present and the future are all enfolded and exist simultaneously.

An equally dazzling concept is that, just as every portion of the hologram contains the image of the whole, every portion of the universe enfolds the whole. This means that every single cell in our bodies enfolds the entire cosmos.

Dennis Gabor

Dennis Gabor (1900-1979) a Hungarian electrical engineer, while working in England to improve the electron microscope, invented a method of storing on film a three-dimensional (3-D) image of the information pattern encoded in a beam of light, i.e., in a visible beam of nonmaterial, subatomic, electromagnetic radiation, and coined the word hologram to describe his discovery. He was the recipient of the 1971 Nobel Prize in Physics.

Conscious Universe

The Time Before Time

By now, you're probably asking: Where did everything contained in the Big Bang come from? And why did it 'Bang' in the first place?

Those questions are indicative of the way Western culture views the word 'creation.' By definition, according to Western thought, creating means 'something' arises from 'nothing.' We erroneously believe that the Big Bang occurred at a specific point in space. But the truth is there was no space for it to explode into. The Big Bang did not expand into existing space; it actually created space and time.

The standard cosmology of the Big Bang, though pervasive, is actually misleading on several points. There is no reasonable explanation, for example, in this theory for the observed flatness and the 'missing mass' of the universe.

There is more gravitational pull in the cosmos than can be accounted for by the existing visible matter. Nearly 99 percent of the universe is dark matter. The other one to two percent is visible, consisting of the stars, galaxies, and literally everything else.

Another misconception is the idea that we can somehow find the 'center' of the universe. As illogical as it seems, the universe contains no center and has no boundaries. No matter how far or wide the high-powered telescopes range in outer space, we continue to find galaxy after galaxy – even in the so-called 'black regions' where previously astronomers believed no stars or galaxies existed.

What we are only now beginning to understand is that the boundaries of 'our universe' may indeed not be the boundaries of 'the universe.' Scientists are seriously contemplating the fact that the cosmos may indeed be infinite in not only time, but also space. It is far more vast – by several magnitudes – than any cosmologist would have dared even to imagine a few decades ago.

Our universe, some physical cosmologists offer, may not be the first or only one to be created. These scientists offer quantitatively elaborate accounts of how the universe we inhabit may have arisen within the framework of a 'meta-universe.' From the Greek work 'meta' meaning 'behind' or 'beyond,' the meta-universe, was the cosmos that existed before ours. Our universe then can no longer be viewed as finite. Instead, it is infinite! Again, this may be another concept that is difficult for Westerns to grasp!

The Big Bang was an explosive instability in the 'pre-space' of the cosmos, a fluctuating sea of virtual energies known by the misleading term vacuum. A region of this vacuum – which is far from the empty space the term implies – exploded, creating a fireball of staggering heat and density.

Within the theory of a one-shot, single cycle universe, this is a particularly vexing proposal. However, when viewed in the context of a cyclic universe, it makes greater sense. It appears more logical that our universe was born in the womb of a metaverse.

Indeed, the search for the ultimate stuff of outer space ends with the discovery that there really is no vacuum, or nothingness. What we previously considered 'empty space' is really, it appears, one giant reservoir of pure energy, a 'quantum sea of light' which cannot be eliminated by the known laws of physics. In a sense, the vacuum and not the 'non-existence' is the beginning and the end of everything in the universe.

'Non-existence' can never be viewed as a source of creation. For many thousands of years, Eastern mystics have held this cosmological view. The Western world, though, is now only beginning to understand it. As a result of profound meditation, the mystics traveled far to provide us with a glimpse of the awesome infinity of the universe that lies beyond.

Indian Vedic mystics view the cosmos as a projection of the Absolute or *Brahman*, rather than of creation. It's a projection of a gross, undifferentiated substance to a subtler one, as opposed to coming into existence from nonexistence.

This means that the Absolute is not separate from creation but is an intimate part of it. Everything that exists in the universe is a manifestation of the Absolute. Everything within the manifest contains a spark of 'singularity.' All life – indeed the entire universe – is seen as a 'unity in diversity.'

There exists nothing other than the Absolute or *Brahman*. The perceiver and the perceived, the individual and the world, the experiencer and the experienced, everything, every being everywhere is the Ultimate Reality, the Supreme Absolute.

Just as a candle can light many more candles, yet its own flame is not diminished, so it is with *Brahman*. The universe emerged from *Brahman*, yet it remains the same. The infinite cosmos is drawn out of the infinite *Brahman*, yet what remains is the infinite *Brahman*. Nothing is lost.

Brahman is not a being, but a state of pure transcendence which is beyond thought. Words fail to describe *Brahman*, whose true nature is simply thought of as *Sat-Chit-Ananda* in the Sanskrit language. Literally, it means Existence-Consciousness-Bliss and it implies that it is eternal, self-aware and blissful. It has no beginning, no middle and no end. It is always existing, because it is existence itself!

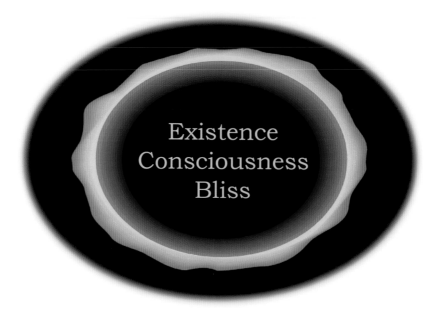

Existence
Consciousness
Bliss

In *Brahman* the universe and its phenomena have not yet begun to be diversified. Though *Brahman* is without qualification, all potency is within it, one with it. It is omnipotent, omniscient, and omnipresent.

The next inevitable question arises: Why does *Brahman* create the universe? And the mystics simply answer: Potency not used, not manifested or projected is no potency at all. If you ask the fire why it produces flames, it will reply, 'I am all flames.' If you ask the ocean why it creates waves, it answers, 'It is no trouble at all.' It is in this sense that the entire universe is said to be in *Brahman*, rises from *Brahman* like numbers from infinity, dwells in *Brahman*, is *Brahman*, returns to *Brahman*.

Maya – the innate power of *Brahman* – elicits the unmanifest into the manifest using two very potent tools: the ability to veil – or conceal – and the ability to project. The positive and the negative aspects of all things yet to come are polarized at this point; the remainder of creation is the interaction between these two extremes. The illusory power of *Maya* is illustrated and demonstrated in the relationship between the Absolute and the manifest.

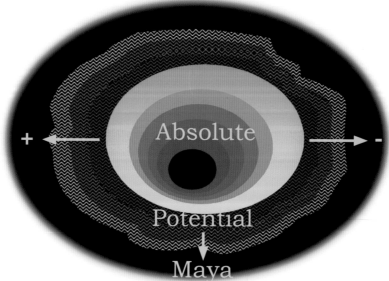

The Transcendental, then, creates the empirical universe. The Absolute enters into a relationship with the relative. The entire universe is to be in, arises from, dwells in, and then returns to *Brahman*.

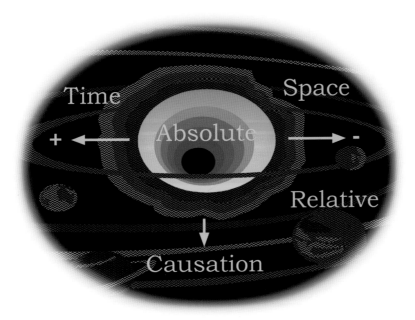

Brahman is one homogenous, unvarying, unfathomable, eternal, all pervading Reality. The wise recognize unmanifest *Brahman* in all manifestations. But our own perceptions of its expressions of creation are many and varied. Just as electricity is one while its ultimate nature is revealed through many forms and uses, so it is with *Brahman*.

At this point *Maya* diverges into two channels, the conscious principle and unconscious material nature. Operating through *Maya*, *Brahman* produces *prakriti* (Matter), the very essence of this universe, which is three-fold: *Sattvic* or unactivity, *rajasic* or activity and *tamasic*, inactivity. These three principles – or *gunas* – exist as unmanifest – or hidden – in total equilibrium in the original *prakriti*. Only when the conscious principle ignites the inner core of *prakriti* is this delicate balance disturbed and the three *gunas* begin to interact.

Then the primal cause passes into the golden womb and the stirrings in *prakriti* produce *mahat*, or magna, the first mass trying to find one or more identities. In scientific terms, this *mahat* corresponds to the nebulous state of matter from which the vortices of energy – or atomic particles – are produced and into which they again coalesce.

The three *gunas* combined with the two polarities within the power of *Maya*, produce all the objective material phenomena of the universe. Not all *prakriti*, though, transform into the objective universe or dark matter. Even though the cosmos, on its surface, appears to be in a state of imbalance, deep within the force of *prakriti's* equilibrium remains intact and at the end of a creation cycle the universe depolarizes to that perfect state of balance once again.

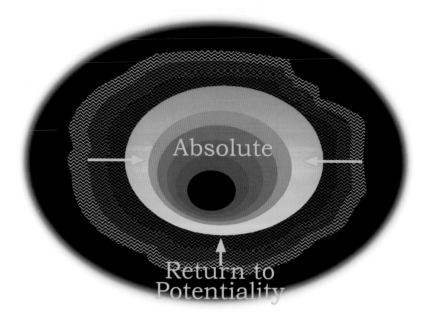

Hindu tradition is not the only ancient culture that viewed the universe in this way. The Buddhist metaphysical term for 'suchness' and 'void' is *Dharma-kaya*. Again, the concept of *sunyata*, 'the void,' that is emptiness or 'suchness,' is not to be taken literally as meaning a vacuum or an equivalent to our idea of nothingness. *Sunyata* is the very source of all life and the essence of all forms.

The Chinese call it the Tao or The Way, the ultimate, indefinable Reality. The Tao is the cosmic process in which all entities are involved. The Chinese culture views the cyclic nature of the world as a continuous change and constant flow. The symbol called T'ai-chi T'u or 'Diagram of the Supreme Ultimate' illustrates the two dynamic archetypal poles of nature, the yin and yang.

Yin

Dark
Rest
Earth
Female
Intuitive
Receptive
Stillness

Yang

Bright
Action
Heaven
Male
Rational
Creative
Movement

Each of us brings with us certain views – forged from our culture, our upbringing, and our personal experiences – to the discussion of this topic. This is inevitable. It does at times though create confusion concerning the differences and the similarities between the Eastern and Western schools of philosophies. Philosophers, theologians and mystics have expressed their thoughts, feelings and revelations about Reality in a myriad of ways. All too often we view these glimpses into infinity with indifference, as if they have little impact on our lives and we go about our daily business as though we have understood nothing. It is difficult, in all truthfulness, for the finite mind to grasp the infinite.

When examined from a distance, the similarities of these systems are astoundingly similar. Perhaps this is because the founding philosophers of all religions had received personal revelations of Reality directly from the Source. Because of this, we can trace a common thread of unity through many divergent systems. Each philosophical system employs its own language to describe the indescribable. As you survey these spiritual concepts, you may find that they have much more in common than what would ever imagine.

In the Vedic tradition, Reality is seen on three planes:

Brahman: the transcendental, absolute, and transpersonal being.

Hiranya-garbha: the golden womb, God, the imminent spirit of the universe, or Ishwara: the Lord, the personal God.

Avatara: the divine incarnate being, such as Jesus, Krishna or Zarathushtra, manifest in history.

The Buddhist philosophers, who call the ultimate Reality as *shunya* – which is not the relative nihil of our simple limited worldly cognition --- see the same reality at three levels.

Dharma-kaya: the transcendental, transpersonal being like *Brahman*

Sambhoga-kaya: the enlightened universal spirit imminent in the universe

Nirmana-kaya: the historical Buddhas who incarnate throughout history

In Christianity we also see a threefold Reality in the Father, the Son and the Holy Spirit.

All philosophies, using seemingly different language, describe the same Reality. A Reality that reveals its true nature only when you blend mysticism and quantum physics. The new physics offers scientific validation for ancient Eastern philosophy.

The ultimate nature of Reality transcends time, space and causation. Time and again the paradoxes encountered in physics reveal this. The existence of reality depends on consciousness, physicists have discovered. Moreover, scientific evidence also seems to reveal that quantum events split the universe into an incomprehensible number of parallel universes.

The true home of consciousness resides in the implicate order, Bohm explains. Thus, the great ocean of consciousness, *Brahman*, which divides itself into all humans exists in all things. We remain ignorant of this oceanic infinity of consciousness just like a fish remains oblivious of the water it swims in. We don't realize that we are swimming in the great ocean of *Brahman*. This consciousness permeates a rock, the grains of sand, and the waves of an ocean, lending meaning to the poem of the mystic Yogiraj Vethathiri:

It moved;
That was the beginning.
Before that, It was silent, static, infinite Truth.
The shimmering was life, energy tumultuous, cradling the atoms.
In the rapturous churning of the centrifugal whirl
They joined and co joined, clashed and exploded
In one volatile splendor.
It was the unfolding;
The massing of constellations, the suns and the stars,
The manifestation of all things animate and inanimate,
The awakening of consciousness
The dance of life between birth and death.
It was communion,
The co-mingling of spirit and flesh
The emergence of man
Conscious of justice and righteousness
Fulfilling himself in awareness
And in service selfless and pure.

Vedas	Buddhist	Christian
Brahman	*Dharma-kaya*	*God, the Father, Logos, the Transcendent Reality*
Hiranya-garbha or Ishvara	*Sambhoga-kaya*	*Holy Ghost, the spirit of the universe*
Avatara	*Nirmana-kaya*	*Son, God in History*

Hinduism

That Hindus 'worship idols' is probably the single most common misconception about Hinduism. Hindus use images as concrete tools to connect with the abstract Divine. They fully understand that the Divine is much greater than the physical image in the temple! They see the unseen through the seen. The million gods and goddesses are only 'anthropomorphized symbols' to represent different diverse faculties e.g. Sarasvati for all arts, Laxami for abundance, Shiva for fertility and so on.

Gunas of Prakriti

The three gunas or qualities born of prakriti or Material Nature in different proportions influence all levels of manifestation. 1.Sattva, the principle of harmony, purity and light, happiness, knowledge, symbolized by the color white. 2.Rajas, the principle of activity, movement, energy, passion, attachment, symbolized by the color red. 3.Tamas, the principle of inertia, stability or stagnation, darkness, ignorance, indolence symbolized by the color black.

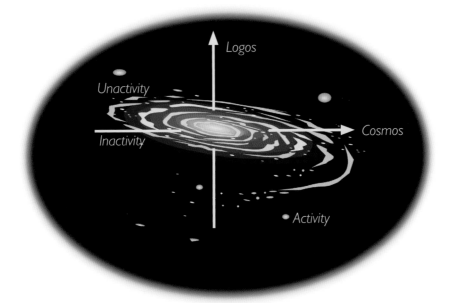

Logos

Unactivity

Inactivity

Cosmos

Activity

Buddha

The Buddha was born as Siddhartha Gautama, a prince of the Sakya tribe in Nepal, in approximately 566 B.C. When he was 29 years old, he left the comforts of his home to seek the meaning of suffering he saw around him. After six years of arduous yogic training, he abandoned the way of self-mortification and instead sat in mindful meditation beneath a bodhi tree for 49 days and nights. His last words were … 'Impermanent are all created things; strive on with awareness.'

Christianity

The idea of the manifest and the unmanifest are illustrated perfectly by the life and death of Jesus Christ.. Jesus, the fully human, person is the manifest: 'The Word became flesh and dwelt among us.' (John 1:14) It is Jesus who died on the cross. Christ, the unmanifest lives forever in each and every individual as the 'Christ Consciousness.'

Cycles of Time

A millennium before Europeans were willing to divest themselves of the Biblical idea that the world was a few thousand years old, the Mayans were thinking of millions and the Hindus billions. The Vedas is the only one of the world's great philosophies dedicated to the idea that the Cosmos itself undergoes an immense, indeed, an infinite, number of deaths and rebirths. It is the only philosophy in which time scales correspond to those of modern scientific cosmology.

—Astrophysicist Carl Sagan, Cosmos

Vedic Cosmology bases its philosophy on the concept of an endless repetition of cycles – each composed of three distinct parts. Initially, the universe generates into existence. This is its unmanifest state prior to creation. It then 'operates,' this part of the cycle is the Creation, which results in the production of finite matter. And lastly, the third part of the cycle is Dissolution, in which the universe returns to its unmanifest state. Once the universe completes its last phase, it is reborn and the threefold nature of the cycle begins again.

It is no coincidence that the cycles of the universe correspond to what the ancient Indian seers saw in the great beings of consciousness. *Brahma* corresponds to the Generator, *Vishnu*, the Operator, and *Shiva*, the Dissolver (*GOD*). These wise men describe the endless cycles that flowed one into another through the vast panoramas of space and time.

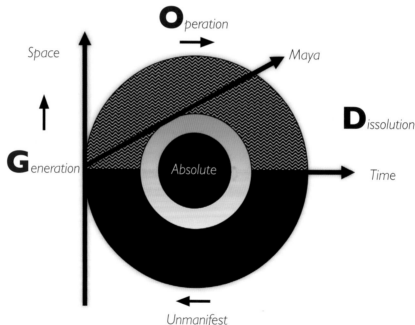

The 'great age' or *maha yuga*, the shortest of these world cycles, is indeed an incredibly long period to us. It takes 2,000 *maha-yugas* to equal one day and one night in the life of the creator, *Brahma*. Three hundred sixty of these days and night, called *kalpas*, compose the life of *Brahma*.

And the length of a *kalpa*? Incredibly long, in Western terms. A common simile which vividly illustrates the time frame of a *kalpa* goes like this:

Suppose that once every hundred years a delicate piece of silk rubs once across a solid rock measuring one cubic mile. When the rock finally erodes because of this action, one kalpa still would not have passed!

Each *maha-yuga*, moreover, is divided into four *yuga*s, with each one lasting a shorter time period than the one before it in a ratio of 4:3:2:1. They are:

- *Satya-Yuga* equals 1,728,000 human years.

- *Treta-Yuga* equals 1,296,000 human years.

- *Dvapara-Yuga* equals 864,000 human years.

- *Kali-Yuga* equals 432,000 human years.

The total years found in one *maha-yuga* is 4,320,000. One *kalpa* equals 8 billion, 640 million years. This means that *Brahma's* total life span is a more than 3 trillion years. Currently, we are in the 51st year of the life of *Brahma*.

Remarkably, these ancient time scales correspond to those of modern scientific cosmology. Its cycles from our ordinary day and night to a day and night of *Brahma*, 8.64 billion years long. Longer than the age of the Earth or Sun and almost half of the time since the Big Bang. And there are much longer time scales still.

In the West, we view time, space and life as linear events. So the creation of the universe – and its end – are viewed as alpha and omega, the two end points defining the linear existence. This theme recurs over and over in our literature, and even occurs in the most popular scientific theory of the creation of the universe, the Big Bang.

Eastern traditions, however, take a nearly diametrically opposed view... Defining the observable universe in terms of a series of cycles repeated endlessly, this became the underpinning for their interpretation of time, space and life itself. Why should people – who are as much a part of the cyclic rhythm of the universe – be any different from every other object in it? Life, then, is considered cyclic as well. Birth and death are merely cycles through which everyone and everything passes. This is the Eternal Return.

If we translate the essence of the Vedic philosophy into Western Scientific terms, we discover a perfect correlation of ideas. The concept of the eternal universe undergoing its endless cycles of creation and destruction can be easily viewed as a blending of science's Big Bang, Plasma Cosmology and its Steady State theory.

Even spirit and matter – customarily thought to be at opposite ends of physical manifestation – can be understood as simply two forms of energy at different ends of the spectrum. Matter is merely a dense version of spirit. Spirit, in turn, is a less dense subtle aspect of matter.

The one element binding it all together is the self-aware energy manifesting itself as consciousness.

This approach to the understanding of the universe therefore places microcosm squarely within the context of macrocosm – not outside of it, as though it was just another point to study. Its definitive quality is its cyclic nature of time, space, and causation. Western scientific thought, it seems, is only now discovering this wealth of ancient knowledge, finally validating the ideas that have been known in the eastern world for thousands of years.

Carl Sagan

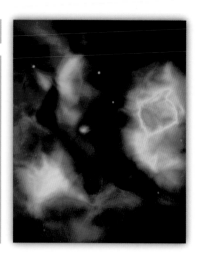

Carl Sagan (1934-1996) did much to popularize science in general and astrophysics in particular. His book, Cosmos, was the best-selling science book ever published in the English language and also the basis of the Emmy and Peabody Award winning television series. He was the David Duncan Professor of Astronomy and Space Sciences at Cornell University. He also received NASA medals for Exceptional Scientific Achievement and for Distinguished Public Service.

Orgin of Vedic Hymns

The earliest Vedic hymns were transmitted orally for thousands of years before being committed to the written word about 500 B.C. The great sages of antiquity 'heard' the verses during their deep sates of meditation (today we might say they 'channeled' them), and then passed them to other Brahmans, the priests who are the custodians of the Vedas since time immemorial. They are almost certainly still being pronounced identically as they were thousands of years ago — with not one word, or even one syllable — lost due to the passage of time.

The Cycles of Time

Each cycle with the maha-yuga is names for the throw of dice. Krita yuga is the winning throw; Treta means you 'almost win.' The cycle Dvapara means you 'nearly lose,' while Kali is the equivalent of being 'wiped out.' Don't be discouraged for being the Kali-Yuga. For even in this phase there are cycles — and things do start looking up!

The Matrix

A King wanted to divide seventeen horses among his three sons in the following manner: one-half to the eldest, one-third to the middle son, and one-ninth to the youngest, but he was unable to do so. One of his ministers offered the king his personal steed to accomplish the division. Eighteen horses were then divided as follows. The eldest son got nine, the middle son received six and the youngest one got two – a total of seventeen. The Minister got his horse back!

17 King's Horses   +   Minister's Horse   = **18**

This is the veiling, concealing and projecting power of *Maya* – the illusion. In fact, the entire matter-space-time matrix is an illusion. The mystics have told us this is true. The idealists have told us this is true.

Now, most interesting of all, the physicists are telling us this is true. All of the ideas we have held concerning the absolute nature of the physical universe are wrong. As we more closely examine the universe, we are confronted with indeterminate forms, which carefully – almost grudgingly – reveal an illusory nature of Reality.

That which makes the immeasurable measurable is called *Maya* – the illusion. Space is not measurable, yet we measure it. It is quantified in our minds. Does the space enclosed in a car sitting stationary in your driveway ride along with you when you drive to the grocery store? Or does it get left behind?

Does the space in a car drive away, or is it left behind?

Space is not measurable, yet it is measured by the mind.

When we move from one room to another in our house, what happens to the space inside us? Does it come along, or does it stay behind? How easily the laws that dictate our three-dimensional world are destroyed in the face of such questions. How easily they become irrelevant.

It is a paradox: measurable yet immeasurable. The laws governing the behavior of the more ponderous levels of reality do not apply as we approach the finer, more ethereal levels of existence. Whenever we pull away from consciousness and move toward the idea of any finite part, we immediately go from the infinite Absolute into the limiting world of *Maya*.

We normally don't recognize this *Maya* because we view ourselves as segregated from our surroundings. However, the true Reality is that the observer and objective reality are one. The observer and observed are interrelated in a real, fundamental sense.

Our only access to the physical world is through experience. The common denominator of all experiences is the 'I' who actually perceives the events. What we experience therefore is not an external reality existing beyond our boundaries as we are so accustomed to thinking. Rather, we are witnesses to our interaction with the physical world.

The concept of 'scientific objectivity' rests, then, upon a false assumption. It assumes that there is an external world 'out there' somewhere and the person observing it – the 'I' – is 'in here'.

As the twentieth century progressed, however, and scientists slowly pried the secrets of quantum physics from the universe, we began to understand that our reality is what we choose to make it.

In our attempts to penetrate the secrets of matter, we have found a glimpse of *Maya* – the 'illogicalnesses' in the architecture of the universe. In fact, this discovery leads us to some rather stunning conclusions concerning the reality of our interconnectedness to the universe. It also reveals the illusory quality of our long held assumptions that an object and its subject are distinctly separate entities. Rather, at a deeper level we are a continuum with all we observe. In some extraordinary sense, *we are they!*

This concept is similar to the holographic paradigm. The holographic image is an illusion as well. The wholeness and unity existing within that realm of the implicate order is the true source from which reality unfolds.

As long as we confuse the matter-space-time matrix with Reality, without sensing the unity of the Absolute underlying all of the forms in the universe, we are transfixed by the spell of *Maya*. This is the root of our inescapable sense of separateness from others and from the environment around us.

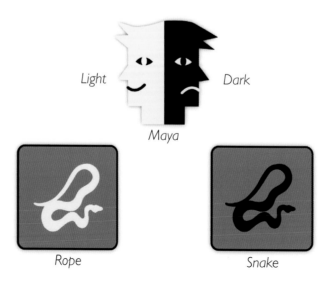

Light   Dark

Maya

Rope   Snake

The illusion lies merely in our perspective; we think the shapes, structure, things, and events around us are realities of nature, instead of recognizing them as only concepts of our measuring, quantifying, and categorizing minds. Confusing our concepts for Reality is like confusing a rope in a dark room for a snake. When the room is darkened, the rope's image can be mistaken for the reptile. However, when the light is turned on the illusion disappears.

Using elements from nature, we can see this illusion at work. Hydrogen in its natural state is a highly combustible substance. Oxygen, likewise, is a necessary ingredient for combustion. But together these two elements create water – which extinguishes fire!

Carbon is an equally fascinating example. Charcoal is carbon; diamond is carbon. However, they are opposites in many ways. Charcoal is black, cheap and a soft substance, leaving marks on paper. Diamonds, however, are brilliant, expensive and cuts through metal and glass.

In the universe at large, there ultimately is no division between the mind and reality. Physicist's recognition of the role of consciousness in the physical universe is a radical departure from classical physics. This, though, is what mystics have taught us for millennia.

The basis of the 'new' physics implies that consciousness itself is not only an intimate part of the physical world, but actually affects the direction of it. All possible realities co-exist until the consciousness edits out the portions our intuition cannot accept.

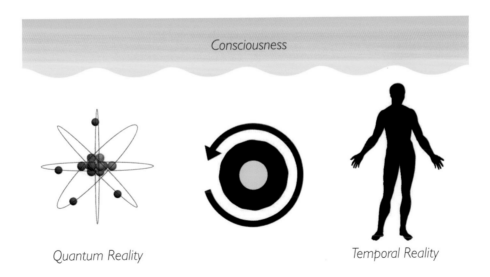

Quantum Reality

Temporal Reality

According to Buddhist tradition, reality is 'virtual' in nature. Objects appearing to be real – like plants and people – are actually nothing more than transient illusions, a result of a limited awareness. The illusion lies in our perception that parts of an overall 'virtual' process are 'real objects.'

Enlightenment, therefore, is the realization that the 'things out there' – including 'I' – are transient, virtual states devoid of separate existence, merely momentary links between illusions of the past and illusions of the future unfolding in the illusion of time.

Achieving enlightenment involves casting off the 'veils of ignorance' so you can perceive directly the inexpressible nature of 'undifferentiated reality.' This is the same Reality we are all a part of, have always been, always will be.

Quantum Reality

Cosmic Reality

The difference is that we look at it in the same way as an enlightened being. To the unenlightened, the physical world consists of many distinct and separate parts. But that does not make them separate. But to the enlightened mystic, who is not caught in the illusion, it is all one. Mystics worldwide have recognized that each moment of enlightenment (grace/insight/Samadhi/satori) reveals that everything – each seemingly separate part of the universe – is but a manifestation of the same whole entity. There is only one Reality, whole and unified. It is one.

True Transcendence

People observe a shoe being made by a shoemaker. A dress being made by a dress maker. A clock being made by a clockmaker. So on. They look at the world and conclude that world must have been made by a world-maker. They believe that someone has created the world. They call him creator. God. But this is only speculation. If you believe that God created this world then you separate God from the created world. You restrict and limit a boundless God. You reduce God to the status of a shoemaker! What a fantastic illusion you are caught up in!

God does not create the world. Creation is God. God is not separate but immanent and omnipresent. God is 'impersonal' and not 'personal.' One cannot own Eternity and Infinity. This concept transcends time, space and causation.

Omnipresent means all-pervading. How can God be separate from the creation? What pervades all space and is infinite cannot move. Stillness is God. Existence itself is God. (Sat)

Omniscient means all knowingness. God is self-aware or self-referral 'all-knowingness.' Consciousness (Chit) is the True Reality. It is all inclusive 'be all and end all' Reality and there being 'no other' delights in itself. Hence blissful. (Ananda)

Omnipotent means all the potency contained therein. Potency not manifested is no potency at all. This is the cause of polarization and all manifestation. (Maya)

Secrets

- Space, time, energy, mass, motion, and gravity are relative.

- An object moves in a four dimensional continuum of space and time – the three dimensions of space and the fourth one of time.

- Time slows down as the speed of light is approached and is nonexistent at light speed.

- We constantly travel between the two parallel universes of external and internal time.

- It is the increase of disorder or entropy that distinguishes the past from the future, giving the 'arrow of time.'

- Einstein's famous equation, $E=mc^2$, proves that energy and matter are inter-convertible.

- The principle of equivalence states that accelerated motion and gravity are equivalent within a frame of reference.

- Gravity is caused by massive objects that warp space-time.

- General relativity predicts that gravity bends light.

- In the Big Bang model of the universe – space, time, matter, and energy were tied up inside the singularity.

- The Steady State theory refutes the Big Bang theory.

- Expansion or contraction of the universe depends on the total gravity of all matter in the universe.

- The main obstacle to developing a theory of everything is the incompatibility of quantum mechanics and general relativity.

- Elementary particles are not considered particles in string theory, but are tiny vibrating loops called strings.

- A string-theory- based 'Theory of Everything' remains an ambition and hope.

- *All manifestation is the result of multiplexing of many overlapping holograms.*

- *The undivided wholeness means everything in the universe is a part of a continuum.*

- *Philosophies, science, and religion all have their roots in the study of the spiritual essence of the universe: Consciousness.*

- *The cosmos is seen as a manifestation of unity in diversity – the veil of illusion (Maya) that prevents us from seeing this is the presence of ignorance and the lack of true knowledge.*

- *The essential nature of the universe is based on cycles.*

- *The laws that apply to the microcosm apply equally to the macrocosm.*

- *Neither our origin nor our disintegration at death is absolute. It is only in a relative sense that any of us are born or die. What is real in us is unborn, undying.*

Microcosm

Microcosm simply means small world. Its origins are from two Greek words: *micros*, for tiny or minute, and *cosmos*, meaning world or universe. The human body symbolizes the microcosm of the universe we live in. All that is within the universe is also within us. As the saying goes, 'We are the stuff the stars are made of.'

There's also another proverb that goes: 'As above, so below.' This profound phrase contains several layers of meaning for us. It recognizes that events on a microscopic level appear to parallel or mirror those on the macroscopic plane, what we call Reality. It also says that as we come to a fuller understanding of ourselves and the Reality within — with ourselves representing the matter 'below,' then we better understand the universe around us — that is what is 'above.'

Biocosm

Origins

How old is the universe? Seventeenth century Archbishop James Ussher calculated the universe was created in 4004 B.C.E. He determined this using clues gleaned from the Bible. If he were correct then today the age of our planet is only 6,000 years. Scientific evidence from the disciplines of astronomy, biology and geology all demonstrate that the Archbishop was wrong. It appears that the universe is unimaginably old and the Earth is much older than a mere 6,000 years.

It is generally accepted in scientific circles that the Earth is nearly 5 billion years old – and the universe itself about three times that age. Moreover, evidence suggests that there really was a definite beginning to the cosmos. This means there is an 'edge' of time.

Scientists believe that the universe was created nearly 15 billion years ago with the Big Bang. About 100,000 years later the first elements of the universe formed – hydrogen and helium – when the cosmos turned into a seething fireball of about 8,000° F (4,000°C).

Features		Years
Civilization	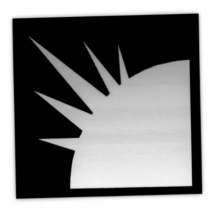	10,000
Mankind		5 million
Mammals		200 million
Terrestrial Life		3 billion
Earth		4.5 billion
Universe		15 billion

Galaxies later formed between one and two billion years after the Big Bang. And our own Sun came into existence about 4.8 billion years ago; our planet 4.6 billion years ago.

Originally, the surface of the Earth was not conducive to any form of life – at least not for the first billion years. Covered with volcanoes spewing out gas and molten rock, the atmosphere created much steam. The steam condensed into water, which in turn fell as rain and created the oceans.

Archbishop James Ussher

Archbishop James Ussher (1581-1656) was highly regarded in his day as a churchman and as a scholar. His treatise on chronology was based on correlation of Middle Eastern history and Holy writ, and was incorporated into an authorized version of the Bible printed in 1701. He established the first day of creation as Sunday 23 October 4004 B.C., concluding that Adam and Eve were driven from Paradise on Monday 10 November 4004 B.C., and that the ark touched down on Mt Ararat on Wednesday 5 May 2348 B.C.

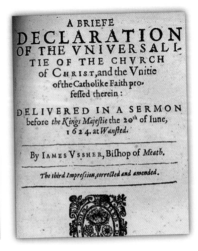

A BRIEFE
DECLARATION
OF THE VNIVERSALL-
TIE OF THE CHVRCH
of Christ, and the Vnitie
of the Catholike Faith pro-
fessed therein:

DELIVERED IN A SERMON
before *the Kings Majestie the 20th of Iune,*
1624. at Wansted.

By Iames Vssher, Bishop of *Meath.*

The third Impression, corrected and amended.

Age of the Universe

The Bible tells us that a bright star appeared in the sky to mark the birth of Jesus Christ. Stars lie so far away from us across space that light from them may take hundreds of thousands of years to reach Earth. The star that was visible on Earth at the time Jesus was born must have flared up centuries before. Such a bright 'new' star may be a supernova or a nova. Its light has to travel across space at a speed of 186,000 miles per second before it reaches the Earth. By the time it does reach this planet, the star may have been dead for hundreds of years. Looking at the stars is like looking back into the past. Because astronomers know how far away stars are, and how long it takes like to travel, they know that the universe is much more than 6,000 years old.

A warm 'soup' of chemicals accumulated in these young waters, leading eventually to the creation of the substance of DNA, which possessed the ability to reproduce itself. Over the next three million years, life on the planet developed. Marine animals filled the seas; insects, amphibians, plant's and the first reptiles populated the land.

Yet, it would still be some time before humans walked onto the timeline of Earth's history. Modern humans descended from ape like creatures that lived in Africa several million years ago. Some time between six and four million years ago, human-like creatures emerged – called hominids – separating their lineage from the apes, the family of primates that today includes chimpanzees, gorillas and orangutans. Hominids stood upright and walked on two legs. There were many different kinds. Over millions of years, they learned to make stone tools, used fire and became successful hunters.

The first modern humans, scientists believe, evolved in Africa and migrated to other areas about 100,000 years ago. And for the last 30,000 years we – Homo sapiens – have been the sole hominid species.

Prebiotic Soup

If God didn't do it this way, then he missed a good bet.

--Harold Urey

So how did life on Earth begin? It's a question that possibly may never be answered with absolute certainty. Scientists have several good theories – as well as replicable experiments to offer us with plausible explanations.

Evolutionists theorize that life sprang from 'non-life' early in Earth's history when a bolt of lightning struck the 'prebiotic soup.' This is the term for the oceans that scientists believed were teeming with chemical compounds. The lightning acted as a catalyst for the chemical reaction that created the most basic form of life.

The 'grandfather' of this research is the Miller-Urey Experiment, named after Stanley Miller, then a graduate student in the Chemistry Department of the University of Chicago and Harold Urey, his advisor, mentor, and partner. Performed more than 50 years ago in 1953, it sought to simulate the conditions scientists think existed on primitive Earth. The goal was to see if life could spring from 'non-life' through the catalyst of lightning.

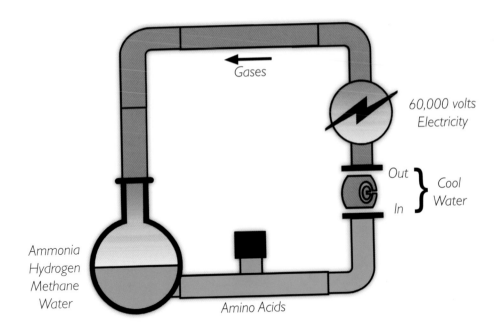

This exercise tested the hypothesis, put forth originally by Aleksandr Oparin and JBS Haldane, that conditions on the young planet were ripe for organic chemicals to arise from non organic ones – in effect that it was possible for life to spring from 'non-life.'

Miller and Urey gathered the molecules believed to be present in the Earth's atmosphere into a closed system: methane, ammonia, hydrogen and water. To simulate the frequent lightning storms of primitive Earth, they ran a continuous electric current through the system. By the end of the first week, nearly 15 percent of the carbon was in the form of organic compounds.

Two percent of the carbons formed amino acids necessary for the production of proteins, including 13 of the 21 used to created proteins in living cells, the most abundant among them being glycine.

This classic experiment showed that the essential components of the creation of life could have been made under the conditions believed to have existed on the young planet.

Harold Urey

Harold Urey (1893-1981) was a chemist whose pioneering work on isotopes earned him the Nobel Prize in Chemistry in 1934 and later led him to theories of planetary evolution. His interests, accomplishments, and influence spanned the disciplines of chemistry, astronomy, astrophysics, geology, geophysics, and biology.

Miller and Urey presented their results at the famous weekly University of Chicago Department of Chemistry seminar where professors and students alike critiqued the experiment. One of the scientists in attendance asked how confident the presenters were that this process actually took place. Urey quickly quipped, 'If God didn't do it this way, then he missed a good bet.'

Excited by the prospect of solving the riddle of the origin of life, other scientists performed their own variations of the experiment. In 1961, for example, Juan Oro created amino acids by placing hydrogen cyanide and ammonia in an aqueous solution. In addition to producing organic compounds, Oro discovered that this situation created an abundance of adenine, one of the four bases of RNA and DNA. Adenine is also a component of adenosine triphosphate, or ATP, a major energy-releasing molecule of the cells. Experiments performed later demonstrated that RNA and DNA bases could also be created through a simulated 'prebiotic' chemistry with a reducing atmosphere.

Similar conditions to those of the Miller-Urey experiments are present in other parts of the solar system, often with ultraviolet light acting as a substitute for lightning as the catalyst for the chemical reactions.

On Sept. 28, 1969, a meteorite fell over Murchison, Victoria, Australia. It contained more than 90 amino acids, 19 of which are also found here on Earth. Comets and other icy bodies from outside the solar system are thought to contain large amounts of complex carbon compounds (such as tholins) formed by these processes. Sometimes this content is so rich that these bodies are dark red or even as black as asphalt.

The heavy bombardment of comets on the early Earth could have possibly provided a large supply of complex organic molecules along with water and other volatiles. These circumstances could imply an origin of life beyond earth, which then migrated here on an errant meteorite.

Recently, scientists have studied the amino acid composition of the genes – defined as those found to be common to organisms from several widely separated species. Up until now, researchers assumed that these organisms shared only the last universal ancestor (LUA) of all extant species.

However, findings indicate that the products of these areas are abundant in those amino acids that are also reproduced in the Miller-Urey experiment. This suggests the original genetic code was based on a smaller number of amino acids – only those, in fact, available in prebiotic nature.

So if God did, indeed, 'miss a good bet,' as Miller quipped during that fateful seminar a half century ago, what other ways were possible for the creation of life? There are several other theories offered that do not require us to take into account the Miller-Urey experiment. One is based on the premise that RNA possesses catalytic properties – those which hasten a reaction which would otherwise occur very slowly. Some evolutionists believe RNA formed by chance from the compounds floating in the prebiotic soup. Its presence was then able to bridge the gap between the first proteins and the first DNA strands.

Others claim that there is fossil evidence for the first one-celled life forms. If indeed there are, then Darwinism would receive a huge boost. Yet another theory contends life first resembled modern 'extremophites', the recently discovered one-celled organisms that dwell in extremely cold or hot conditions. The ability of scientists to sequence the genomes of living organisms allows them to reach this conclusion.

Energy to Matter

How energy relates to matter is analogous to how consciousness relates to physicality. The apparently paradoxical wave-particle duality of subatomic elements, like electrons, actually mirrors the relationship between energy and matter. Einstein in the early 1900s, eloquently explained this relationship with his $E=mc^2$ equation.

Matter and energy, far from being the opposing forces they were once thought to be, are actually compatible, interchangeable entities. Matter can be converted to energy, energy to matter. At the actual point that the conversion occurs, the subatomic particles slow down, densify, and give the illusion of solidity. Yet at the same time they retain some wave-like characteristics.

Visualize a fast-moving beam of light. As it slows down, it begins to solidify until the light actually stops, in effect, 'freezes.' Now it is a 'packet of frozen light.' Our much larger, macroscopic illusion of solid matter – or what we call the physical world – melts away when we delve into the subatomic world of particles. The atom, we have seen, is composed mostly of empty space. The minute 'frozen' subatomic particles fill the void. Matter then is 'frozen energy' and not solid.

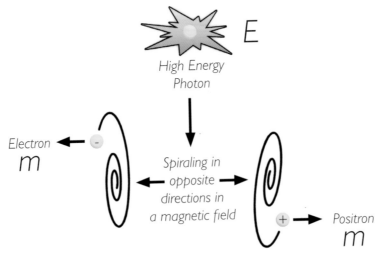

E

High Energy Photon

Electron
m

Spiraling in opposite directions in a magnetic field

Positron
m

This understanding of *matter* as a *specialized energy 'field'* is a revolution. It is also the departure from conventional 'Newtonian' wisdom to what is called the 'Einsteinian' paradigm.

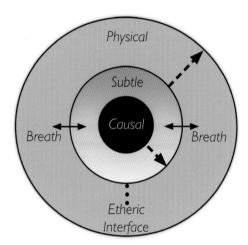

Remarkably, this scientific explanation of matter – pulled from the pages of quantum physics – validates what ancient *Vedas* have said for centuries. They use the term 'vibrational densification' to describe this phenomenon. It explains the subtle energy fields underlying and contributing to the functions of the human physical body.

These energy fields are in dynamic equilibrium and, like radio and television waves, they travel through the same space without interference. Subtle energy differs from physical matter only in the speed of frequency of its vibrations.

In their natural states hydrogen and oxygen exist as separate elements. Combined, though, through natural forces like heat and gravity, they form water vapor. The vapor cools and condenses into water and with even further cooling, the water changes to ice.

In the unmanifest state, only potential energy exists; two elements have yet to form anything. When the two are subject to certain forces, though, the energy manifests in the newly created forms of vapor, water and ice.

The creation of the first causal body, in the process of human manifestation, is comparable to water vapor. It envelops the source, or Spirit, the unmanifested potential energy of pure awareness.

The condensation from vapor to water can be likened to the formation of the subtle body or mind and the creation of ice, is akin to the corporeal or physical body.

Water is denser than vapor. Ice is the densest of the three states and gives the illusion of an impenetrable solid as our bodies do. The subtle energy fields generate matter and not the other way around. Hence, *the body is an extension of the mind.*

The complete human organism, according to Vedic philosophy, consists of *Atman*, or pure Self. The pure Self or the Spirit is the self-aware energy ... *ever free, ever pure and ever wise.* The Self is first encased in the causal body – the 'I-awareness' of the individual. Then it is encapsulated within the subtle body of the mind and finally the gross body – our sensory-dependent physicality. At each point of encasement our vibrational frequency slows. But always within our corporeal bodies exist the highest vibrational frequency that we call our pure Self.

The conversion of energy into matter has been observed and captured in the photographic records of cloud chambers in experimental nuclear facilities. A cosmic ray-a highly energetic photon of light-when passing in the vicinity of a heavy atomic nucleus, leaves its imprint on film as it spontaneously becomes a particle/antiparticle pair. The photon changes form to become two mirror-image particles. Literally, energy becomes matter.

Schema of Creation

Maya diverges into two channels, the conscious principle and the unconscious material nature, as we explained earlier. Operating through *Maya*, *Brahman* produces *prakriti* (Matter), the very essence of this universe, which is three-fold: *sattvic* or unactivity, *rajasic* or activity and *tamasic*, inactivity.

These three principles, or gunas, exist as unmanifest, in total equilibrium in the original *prakriti*. Only when the conscious principle kindles the inner core of the unconscious principle or *prakriti* – and the equilibrium is disturbed – do these *gunas* begin to interact with each other. Combine this with the two polarities with the power of *Maya* – veiling and projecting – and all the objective material phenomena of the universe are produced.

Prakriti provides a body for the Spirit that the personal God. Not all of *prakriti* serves to become the objective universe, much of it remains in a pure relationship to serve as the body of *Karana-Ishvara*, God, the primal cause. This is consistent with the unseen universe, or dark matter.

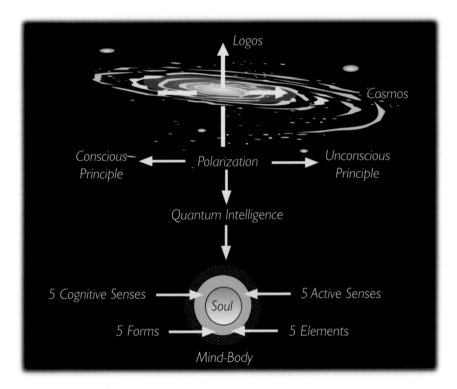

The universe is in a state of disequilibrium. At the end of a cycle of creation, the universe returns to a state of equilibrium once more. The primal cause devolves into the golden womb; the stirrings in *prakriti* produce *mahat* – the magna – the first nebulous mass seeking an identity – or a set of identities.

The union of the gold womb and the *mahat* creates the most important cosmic personality, the universal *buddhi* or cosmic consciousness, identified as a universal person. Alter beings then partake of the *buddhi*. If it were not for this vast *mahat* – or cosmic intelligence – no further individuation could occur. Individuation is much like vortices developing in the cosmic waters of both the conscious and unconscious principles.

The principle of *ahamkara*, the I-maker, flows from *mahat*. The I-maker is the cosmic ego. It is here the process of false identification fully crystallizes. The personality says, 'This is I' when it refers to the material body. The ego assumes forms and names and possesses the limiting attributes associated with it instead of taking on the unlimited, unmanifest power.

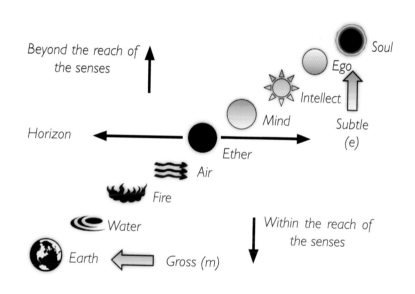

The shining ones derive their bodies from the *sattvic*. The *sattvic* ego, also called the *vaikarika*, produces the mind.

Some authorities believe the cognitive senses, that is, those such as sight, hearing and the like are also produced from this *sattvic* ego. Similarly, these authorities also believe the abilities of the active senses – for example, the hand, feet and organs of speech, generation and elimination – are produced from the *sattvic* ego as well.

Most Eastern philosophers are in agreement, however, that the *bhutadi*, or the *tamasic* ego, produces the subtle elements. These are the refined principles behind our awareness of sigh, sound, touch, taste and smell. Our subtle sense become actual, objective experiences through contact with the senses. These elements are called *tan-matras*.

Authorities are also in agreement concerning the *rajasic* ego, responsible for the necessary movement of the *sattvic* and *tamasic* egos to produce their efforts. Some think the *sattvic* ego is produced by the mind alone. These same authorities also believe the *rajasic* ego produces both the cognitive and active senses.

All the matter in the universe that we see in tangible physical form first began as a subtle more refined object. The five subtle elements we spoke of earlier are called *tan-matras*. From these we get the five gross elements of Earth, water, fire, air and space. These do not signify the actual entities but are metaphors for the five states of matter: solid, liquid, luminous, gaseous and spatial. Space is not regarded as simply emptiness; it is an actual state of matter. They also represent our psychological perception of these states.

This phenomenon develops through the interactions of *sattva*, *rajas* and *tamas* between the positive and negative polarities. All objects in the world as well as our mental attributes are derived from an interaction of these – and none other.

Fields of Life

The subtle energy template that encases our physical matter is never subject to decay. The 'phantom pain' experienced by an amputee also explains the existence of a residual energy template. Even after a limb is removed, patients report sensation of pain in the area where the now-amputated body part once existed!

A unique experiment using electro-photography provides evidence of the subtle body. When this type of photograph is taken of a leaf, with a portion of the leaf missing, the field around the leaf still reveals it to be a whole plant with all parts intact.

In 1940, the neuroanatomist Harold S. Burr of Yale University, conducted research on this field around various living organisms, one of them being the salamander. Using this photographic technique, he was able to map the electrical field of this animal's embryo during the very early stages. Injecting ink into the unfertilized egg's axial region, he discovered something quite remarkable.

His initial expectation was to find an electric field that outlined the shape of the developing egg. However, that was not the case. The field that encased the embryo was the shape of an adult animal.

He continued his studies along this vein, only extending it to seedlings. He found that the electrical field around these sprouts, not the shape of the original seed, but the shape of the adult plant it would someday become.

Burr's accumulated date suggests that both developing plants and animals are destined to follow a template of prescribed growth, determined by the organism's individual electromagnetic field. It acted much like a blueprint of the physical body.

He is most well known for his claim that all living things are molded and controlled by electro-dynamic fields, which he named 'fields of life' or L-fields.

The findings of Allen Detrick and Ion Dumitrescu, who also used this technique for the same reason, should come as no surprise.

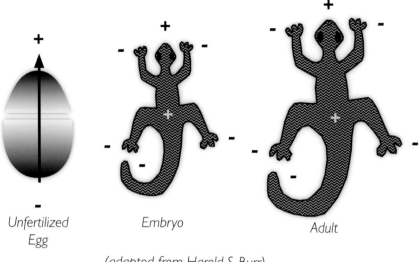

Unfertilized
Egg

Embryo

Adult

(adapted from Harold S. Burr)

Detrick, took the leaf of an adult plant and cut a section out of one of its sides. Then he subjected it to this electro-photography. He found, much to his surprise, that the field around the leaf created a picture of a whole, undamaged leaf. From this photo, there was no evidence of a section being broken off. He dubbed this as 'the phantom leaf effect' and showed the phantom trick on both sides of the leaf, displaying the three-dimensional spatial and organizational nature of such a bio-energetic field--one that is holographic in nature.

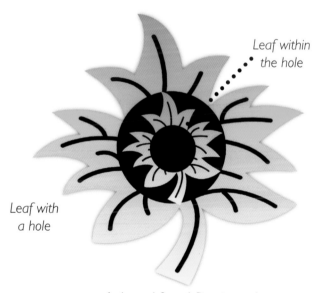

Leaf within
the hole

Leaf with
a hole

(adapted from I. Dumitrescu)

By the same process, Ion Dumitrescu cut a circular hole in a leaf and produced a leaf within a leaf, also confirming the holographic nature of energy fields that surround all living things.

Harold Saxton Burr

Harold Saxton Burr (1889-1973) was E.K. Hunt Professor Emeritus, anatomy at Yale University School of Medicine. He was a member of the faculty of medicine for forty-three years and published, more than ninety-three scientific papers. He was a landscape painter as well as a professor in the Yale University school of Fine Arts from 1939 to 1949.

Electro-photography

This is a technique whereby living objects are photographed in the presence of a high frequency, high voltage, low amperage electrical field. This technique was largely pioneered by the Russian electrician Semyon Kirlian(1900-1980) from whom the process has acquired its name: Kirlian Photography. Kirlian's first research began in the early 1940s at about the same time Burr was measuring electromagnetic fields around living objects.

Subtle Body

Some flesh to eat, a beautiful woman, and a corpse –
So the same body is seen three ways,
by a wolf, a passionate youth, and a yogi.

-- a Sanskrit verse

In the the metaphysical realm, the energy field that surrounds and pene¬trates living systems is referred to as the 'subtle body:' It is said that the subtle body is one of many bodies contributing to the final expression of the human form. The subtle body, in all likelihood, is an energy inter¬ference pattern similar to a hologram.

The complete human organism, Vedic philosophy explains, consists of the *Atman*, pure Self, or Spirit. It is the part of us closest to universal reality despite the fact it remain carefully hidden by the other 'superficial' entities that make up a human being.

The innermost covering of the soul, or pure Self, is the causal body or the 'knower.' The immediate envelope is the subtle body or the 'mind' and the outermost cloak is the gross – or physical – body.

The physical body is the realm of matter that is influenced by time, space, and causation. Subject to entropy and death, we have long understood the workings of this part of our being. It perishes at death. The subtle and causal sheaths, however, are carried forth through countless lifetimes.

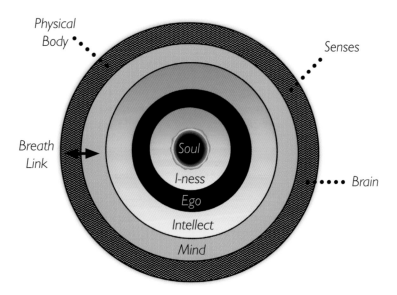

Our physical body is a lot like computer hardware, while our subtle body can be likened to software. The 'artificial intelligence' of the software can be downloaded from one system to another through cyberspace, and thus reincarnate, actually coming into a new 'body.' Similarly, the 'natural intelligence' can transmigrate and remanifest.

So the subtle and causal bodies act as the home to the Spirit. If our body and mind work together, why doesn't the subtle body die with the physical one? The causal body is the field of the 'I' awareness, which is in close proximity to the pure Self, and is the expression of the blissful, dreamless sleep state and the realm of meditation.

It is the subtle body, or the 'global mind' that remains a mystery. Scientists are still asking themselves the same questions the masters did thousands of years ago: How can we prove the existence of the mind when we can not see it? What exactly is contained in the mind?

As invisible as ether, the subtle body is an air-like medium, which remains unseen to the naked eye. Radio, television and X-rays were once unseen phenomenon until developing technology unveiled them. Technology is still in its infancy in its attempt to provide scientists with a glimpse of this higher energy field.

The marriage of computer technology to the X-ray has produced the CT Scanner, which can also provide previously invisible images of electrical energy fields in humans. Technology such as the PET (Positive Emission Tomography) and MRI opens the windows even providing highly detailed cellular pictures of organ structure and function. MRI capitalizes on the magnetic properties of the body's 'etheric interface' energy system...the same system that the Vedic Masters uncovered thousands of years ago without all this fancy equipment!

In meditation, they opened their 'divine eye', and decoded the microcosmic hologram. The described subtle body made of several ingredients: I-Consciousness, intellect, ego, mind, the five cognitive senses, the five faculties of action and their psychological correlates. The subtle body corresponds to the dream state and we find it hard to perceive that it even exists at all.

Our mind, invisible to the naked eye, is composed of both an internal and external instrument. What we refer to as the internal instrument has four ingredients: the individual consciousness, the intellect, ego, and the logical, linear-thinking mind.

The individual consciousness is our limited reflection of the pure Self. We are one part of the whole universe, even if we usually only acknowledge the reality of what immediately surrounds us. From such a limited viewpoint the world seems to revolve around us. From the universal vantage point, the truth is that we revolve with the world.

The intellect links the subtle body to the causal body. It represents our translogical intuitive comprehension. The storehouse of the conscious memory, it also houses our unconscious subliminal impressions. We call upon the intellect, for example, when we need to recall information while taking a test to give us the appropriate answers.

The subtle body is also home to the ego. Prompted by our subconscious impulses, the ego seeks out experiences in the world which satisfy it. The ego-self often serves as the source of our mental afflictions and emotional troubles. The ego, or 'CEO', regularly forgets who the real President of the company is--the pure Self--and likes to run the show according to its own rules.

Directly derived from the intellect, the ego handpicks what it likes and dislikes in the world, making the necessary arrangements with the memory banks. An entirely thought-bound entity, it is conditioned by the need to preserve its own pseudo-existence. If we want to be considered by others as intelligent, our ego-self will seek out situations and relationships in which we seem superior. Perhaps our physical appearance is important; the ego will confine itself to times and places in which we outshine others.

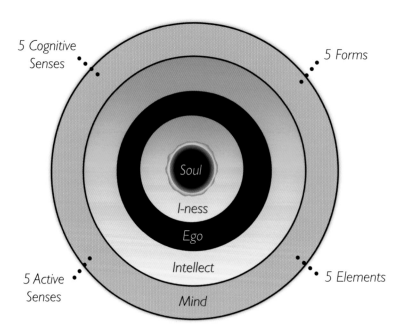

Out of the ego emerges the concept of the linear-thinking mind. It serves the ego by coordinating the functions of the sense and faculties. It sorts, labels, and classifies enormous everyday sensory data, and also works closely with the intellect and the ego in the decision-making process.

Our consciousness, our intellect, our mind and our ego all act together. Collectively, they comprise the inner psychic shell covering the pure Self. Forming the innermost center of our personality, this deeply conditioned instrument seems to control us more than we control it.

Contained in the subtle body are also the potentials for ten faculties of perception and action. They are labeled as external instruments because their outwardly functions are apparent. Our five cognitive senses of perception are hearing, sight, smell, taste and touch. Their corresponding physical organs are the five faculties of action: the power of speech, grasping, motion, reproduction and excretion, which have the corresponding organs of tongue, hands, feet, genitals and rectum. The senses are connected to the gross matter through their physical counterparts.

The internal instrument interprets what we receive and assimilate through the external instrument. Our 'global mind,' or the subtle body that operates directly through the ten faculties, links the external and the internal instruments.

As invisible as ether, the subtle body is an air-like medium, which remains hidden to the naked eye. Considerable evidence suggests that a holographic energy template, or subtle, body, exists associated with our physical body. And the 'etheric interface' the subtle body makes with the physical one has been proven scientifically in various experiments.

Bioenergetic Spectrum

Thanks to the efforts of Dr. William Tiller, professor emeritus of material science at Stanford University, we have a modern model of our bioenergtic fields. This leader in the field of subtle energies divided the mental body into three different levels: instinctive, intellectual and spiritual.

Interestingly enough, this scientist's model fits nicely with Vedic philosophy. The 'astral', 'instinctive', and the 'intellectual' bodies parallel the subtle body, while the 'spiritual' corresponds remarkably well to the causal body. The physical body is linked – via an 'etheric interface' – to the subtle body. Each of these subtle bodies has a bell-shaped distribution of energies.

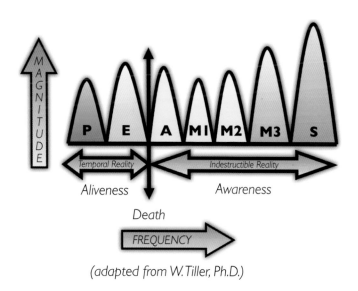

(adapted from W. Tiller, Ph.D.)

Beyond this they act as vehicles for our mobile awareness, like waves in the ocean. When we sleep and dream, these waves of awareness are submerged in the ocean, concealed from us. But when we awaken, the waves ascend into the physical body. The dreamless sleep state is the realm of the causal body.

What we see around us during our waking hours is but a reflection. It's not the final realization. During our deep sleep, we barely touch the source. We continuously fall back into the experiences of the dream and waking states, which occur like tidal waves destroying the mirrored reflection of the pure Self.

The corporeal body – the part that we so often mistake for our identity – would not exist were it not for the energizing nourishment and spatial guidance of the 'etheric interface.' This model is with us from the birth of our physical bodies. It is literally an invisible net – the spatial outline of a human being cradling our body and surrounding us until we die.

Because the physical body and its 'etheric interface' are so tightly interwoven and interdependent, the pair forms what Tiller calls the Human Temporal Reality. 'Aliveness' refers to our earth-bound and time-bound frame of reference and our own physical perspective of reality. It is subjected to the laws of time, space, causation and gravity and hence, it's subject to decay or what scientists call positive entropy.

In contrast, Human Indestructible Reality – or awareness – refers to the areas of our being which are beyond time, space and the physical world. The subtle energetic bodies outside the realm of the 'etheric interface' are indestructible and therefore demonstrate negative entropy.

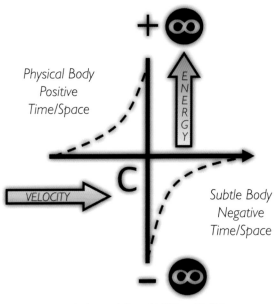

(adapted from W. Tiller, Ph.D.)

The vibrational frequencies of the subtle and causal bodies are *supraluminal*. They fall into the domain of negative time, negative space and negative entropy. Tiller, using Einstein's equation, predicts the existence of faster-than-light energy, which has magneto-electrical properties. These subtle energies are not easily detectable or measurable by conventional means, since the human limit of observation stops short at the speed of light – 186,000 miles per second.

Awareness and Aliveness

Treating humans without the concept of energy is treating dead matter.

-- Albert Szent-Gorgy, Nobel Prize Laureate, Hungary (1893-1986)

Ancient wisdom celebrates unity in diversity, acknowledging that everything is grounded in one reality. We are, indeed, a microcosm – a self-contained small world inside a macrocosm – or the whole – as Eastern philosophers have long understood. What is within us mirrors the entire universe. Likewise, whatever is in the universe mirrors what is inside us. When we truly understand this and are able to relate to this concept then we will be closer to the forces of creation.

Diversity in unity is a fact that scientists are only now coming to appreciate as they approach a general unified theory. Their progress in high-energy physics already has led to unified theory of the fundamental forces of electro-magnetism and gravity. They have concluded, in fact, that a single *unified field* is, indeed, the basis of all diversity in nature. This revelation echoes the teachings of Eastern wisdom.

In other words we – like every other physical entity in the universe – are energy. Actually, we are the product of two types of energy. The first is our potential energy of *awareness*. This type is ever-evolving. The second is dynamic energy or the *aliveness* within us. This latter version powers the corporeal needs of our gross body, which constantly needs to be replenished from outside sources: air, water, food, and sunlight. When we sleep, this energy is restored. Both energy fields – awareness and aliveness – must integrate harmoniously and remain in balance to maintain order in our complex system.

In other words, *we are energy* and *we need energy*. The recognition that all matter is energy thus becomes the foundation for understanding how we are considered complex energy system.

Within the human microcosm, the static or potential energy of awareness is called chit. Never subject to disorder or entropy, chit is an ever-renewing and ever evolving energy system.

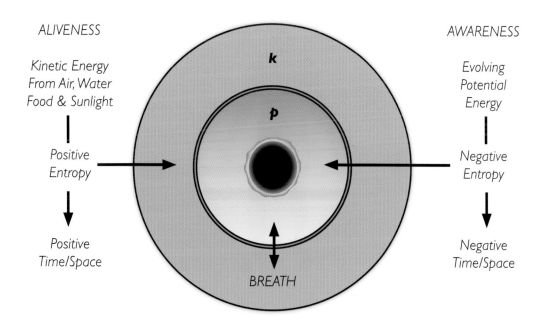

In his extensive work, Nobel-prize winner Ilya Prigogine, defined the law of thermodynamics, and saying that entropy is only valid if the machine is a closed-energy system. When this is applied to the open energy system of the human brain, Prigogine insisted that human awareness is not subject to entropy or decay. Awareness is negatively entropic.

The dynamic energy or the working force of the physical body is called the *prana* or the aliveness. *Prana* flows like fluid energy through an intricate network of channels called *nadis*, connecting the body to the mind. Prana keeps the entire organism is working order. The Japanese call it *ki* and the Chinese call it *chi*.

Prana – unlike *chit* – is subject to entropy. It needs constant nourishment or replenishment. Our bodies cannot survive without the essentials that maintain our physical bodies in a balanced and working order. Without food, water and the other essentials our bodies eventually decay and die. Aliveness is positively entropic.

Order to disorder. Our aliveness – not our awareness – is subject to conditions and decay. Our awareness is indestructible and continuous. This 'breakthrough' concept has yet to be fully understood and applied by conventional medicine.

Physical matter is nothing but an illusion of the senses. Both Vedic philosophy and now quantum physics realize this. Matter is composed of particles which are nothing more than 'frozen light.'

Intangible, abstract entities like energy are admittedly difficult to comprehend. They are the unseen forces behind the mechanisms themselves. There is an unseen connection between the body and the subtle forces of spirit. It is the relationship between matter and energy that seers found enlightening. They not only understood this partnership, but used it to maintain optimal health.

Human beings are more – much more --than merely a collection of chemicals, organs, flesh and bones. What distinguishes us from non-living systems is that we are greater than the mere sum of our parts.

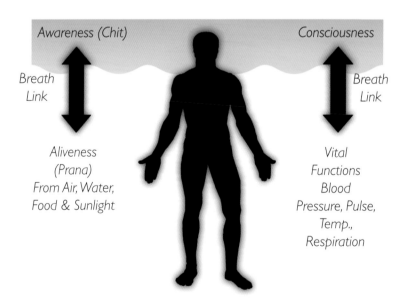

Science is an ever evolving search for further knowledge. Newton, for example, studied acceleration and gravity. From this, he deduced various laws of motion based on nature. Scientists, working on his knowledge and experiments, then predicted how mechanical systems would behave. Newton's models, however, were unable to explain the behavior of electricity and magnetism. Neither could they account for the role of energy in living things. New models of the universe were developed to explain how energy phenomenon relates to life.

Scientists are uncovering the unseen forces of energy, much like the ancient Vedic philosophers unveiled these same powers before them. Contemporary scientists are now looking at the body as both an instructional model and an energy field. They are discovering that human awareness is a field of energy. Not only that, but this awareness is intimately integrated to the physical body. Human awareness, moreover, actively participates in the creation of health – or in the creation of illness.

With this revelation, our understanding of the human body changes forever. Now we are truly viewing the intimate interconnectedness of the body, mind and spirit. A full understanding of the concepts of both awareness and aliveness solves the puzzle of why some people seem immune to ill health and other are continuously subject to ailments and disease. The prana can be enhanced through proper diet, exercise and restful sleep. Meditation however is the best medication for awareness.

The universal macrocosm and the human microcosm are both grounded in the same Reality – and that makes them inexorably intertwined.

Ilya Prigogine

Ilya Prigogine (1917-2003) was awarded the Nobel Prize in chemistry in 1977 for his scientific work in understanding the role of time in the physical sciences and biology. He was born in Moscow, Russia and obtained his education at Universite Libre de Bruxelles. He received numerous international awards and 53 honorary degrees.

Circle
of Life

Fertile Field

The voyage that ends in the creation of life is truly miraculous. Each human life begins as a single, microscopic cell before it is transformed into a fully developed fetus. The key element in this fantastic voyage of life is the fertilization – or the great awakening – of the egg. This process has been compared to 'Sleeping Beauty,' the classic fairy tale, where the young maiden is awakened from a deep slumber by Prince Charming's kiss.

The egg is awakened from its dormant state by the events of fertilization which leads to the process of egg activation. Fertilization occurs when the sperm and ovum both enter the ampulla of the fallopian tube. As the tail of the sperm falls off, its head and neck fuses with the ovum. The result is an egg that is protected by an impenetrable lining.

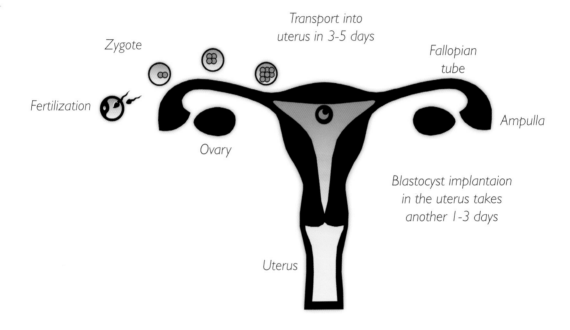

Zygote

Transport into uterus in 3-5 days

Fallopian tube

Fertilization

Ampulla

Ovary

Blastocyst implantaion in the uterus takes another 1-3 days

Uterus

An additional 3 to 5 days are needed following fertilization for transport of the ovum – now called the zygote – through the rest of the fallopian tube in the cavity of the uterus. The delayed delivery is no accident. During this time several stages of cell division occur. The zygote grows into a hollow ball of about 100 cells and is now called a blastocyst as it enters the uterus.

The blastocyst usually stays in the uterus cavity for another 3 to 5 days before it becomes implanted into the uterine wall. Implantation ordinarily occurs between the fifth to seventh day after ovulation.

In approximately 10 days – less than two weeks from the start of this journey – the blastocyst is completely implanted in the lining of the uterus, where finally the nutrients of the mother nourish it.

The adjacent cells rapidly multiply once implantation has taken place, forming the placenta and the various membranes of pregnancy. The placenta begins to provide nutrition after about the sixteenth day beyond fertilization – or a little more than a week following implantation.

Unification

Until the blastocyst actually implants for conception in a womb, it remains 'alive but unaware' and in itself not able to grow into an embryo even though it is fertilized.

In vitro fertilization is a perfect example of this. An ovum and sperm are mixed in a glass laboratory dish. It stays in this temperature-controlled environment for about 2 ½ days before the physician transplants it into the mother's uterus. Its growth continues only if the implantation is successful. Only then can the pregnancy progress.

The fertilized cells can be kept 'alive' for long periods if they are not implanted. These can be used for stem cell research. These specialized cells are in a state that make them capable of dividing and renewing themselves, but they remain nonfunctional without transplantation.

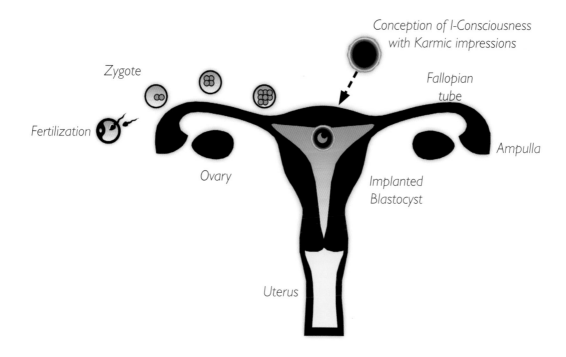

The dual process of fertilization and implantation ensures the egg a continued supply of nutrients – aliveness or *prana* – and generates the required 'fertilized field' ready for conception.

In its subtle realm this field contains the unseen holographic 'thought imprint' of the maternal and paternal impressions. The transmigrating I-Consciousness or awareness as well as its Karmic imprint are conceived into this 'fertilized field.' This heralds the beginning of growth and development. It really is, then, a union of three – not two – that defines life.

The prenatal stage of development begins only at the time of conception and continues until the birth about 39 weeks later. From the fourth month of gestation, every organ system is in place and functioning, at which point, development is mainly a matter of growth.

Spatial Orientation

How do these newly differentiated cells know to travel and where their appropriate spatial locations are in the developing fetus? That continues to be one of the greatest mysteries of biology. DNA fails to explain this spatial organization of cells.

What is an even more elusive concept is the manner by which these cells know exactly where to place themselves in each stage of the process. How do the cells know to become an arm, or a leg? What are the actual mechanics which allow these cells to group and assemble themselves into a three-dimensional human form?

At this point, all we can do is make several educated speculations. It's very likely that the cells follow a complex three-dimensional map or holographic template. Some have called this the 'etheric body', a field carrying the coded information necessary to transform the fetus into a human being.

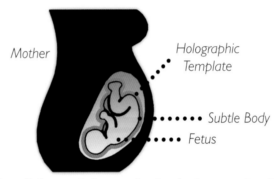

It also acts as a road map for cellular repair in case the developing organism is damaged. Just as the genetic code of the DNA directs the cell differentiation, the 'etheric body' unfolds the spatial orientation.

Renowned English clairvoyant Geoffrey Hodson, lent credence to the idea of an etheric predecessor of the actual physical body. He undertook the extraordinary attempt to investigate a developing human embryo from the point of conception up until birth.

Hodson documented the prenatal etheric mold that appears shortly after conception. This etheric matter is actually a sketch plan of the human body. Hodson, employing his supernatural sense of 'clear vision,' saw the holographic energy fields inside the mother's womb. He 'watched' as they settled into their appropriate places within the growing body.

Rev. Geoffrey Hodson

Rev. Geoffrey Hodson (1886-1983) is the most well known clairvoyant among Liberal Catholics. He verified from his own inner experience the effectiveness of the Science of Yoga in uplifting and expanding human consciousness. During his long life he had worked with several scientists who stood in admiration of Mr. Hodson's clairvoyant abilities. In his book 'The Miracle of Life' he made clairvoyant observations during the nine months of pregnancy.

Chakras and Development

Genetic memory requires the unbroken passage of genetic material throughout many generations. Memories of past lives do not follow a genetic trail. People recall lives from all eras, and all regions of the world, which would imply multiple genetic histories. No genetic line is followed; in fact, it is repeatedly disrupted.

How can these memories be recalled from one life to the next with no single source of genetic material from which to pull?

The answer lies in the subtle body template, which during embryogenesis, acts as a blueprint for the human body. The *chakras* are also formed here. *Chakras* are vortices of 'carried over' indestructible, subtle energies from past life experiences. The newborn – the incarnating soul – is influenced by the karmic impressions of past desires, instincts, action, behavior and deeds.

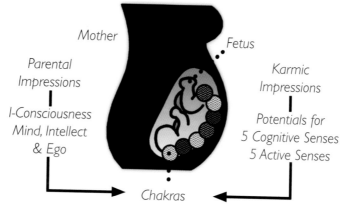

The *chakras*, therefore, are the energy repositories of karma and are bound by the law of cause and effect. If they do not provide the necessary sustaining energies to the developing organs, there is a breakdown at the cellular, physical level. Perhaps a person could not express love or compassion in a previous life. He conveyed 'hard-heartedness.' In his current life, this may surface in the form of a severe blockage in the heart *chakra* which would show up in a newborn as a congenital heart defect.

Besides these karmic impressions, the *chakras* are also the reservoir for the 'carried over' I-Consciousness, Mind, Intellect, Ego, five cognitive and five active sense *potentials* instrumental in the growth and development of the fetus. This transference from past to present only occurs at the *chakra* level.

Death Transition

The body of Benjamin Franklin, printer, like the cover of an old book, its contents torn out and stripped of its lettering and gilding, lies here, food for worms, but the work shall not be lost. For it will appear once more in a new and more elegant edition, revived and corrected by the author.'

         – Benjamin Franklin, writing his epitaph, at age twenty two.

What we call death is not a process that is separate from birth and life. It is intimately related to birth and life. Carlisle once said that every author has a right to call black white as long as he is consistent in his use. I will refer to the process of 'birth,' 'new birth,' and 'rebirth' as death, only to adhere to general convention.

Continuity of consciousness following physical death is accepted by nearly all modern thinkers. Most recently, Dr. J.B. Rhine, professor of parapsychology at Duke University, has acknowledged its existence. Death, more of us are realizing, is not the end of life, but rather a transition to an 'after state.'

Energy can never be created or destroyed, only transformed. When we die our energy is not destroyed into 'nothingness.' It must be transformed, changed, or moved in some fashion to obey one of the most fundamental laws of nature. *Only what is alive can die. What is aware can only become unaware.*

Our dying severs the energy link of *prana* or 'aliveness' between the subtle and the gross body. It is moved – in the form of dissociated aliveness or kinetic energy and returned to the free energy of the universe, while the corporeal body returns to the elements.

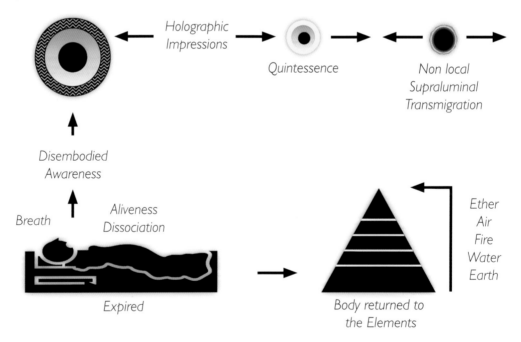

This indestructible energy field of 'awareness' shifts from the physical to the subtle and causal bodies. At the moment of our death, our lives flash before our eyes as a panorama of memories. Dr. Raymond Moody, of the University of Virginia, has documented this phenomenon of 'life review' accomplished in an instant of earthly time – in the near-death experience (NDE) in his book 'Life After Life.'

NDE is perhaps the most dramatic evidence we have for life after death and the existence of the nonphysical world. A universal phenomenon, NDE is amazingly experienced by each and every person in the same way. These people report 'seeing the light,' who they say is actually a 'being' of light. Rather than being a terrifying experience, everyone who has undergone a near-death experience reports that the light, in addition to being indescribably brilliant, is incredibly comforting as well. There is no sense of physical body —only an awareness of the mind. This disembodied awareness encapsulates the 'light' – or pure Self – and in fact comes to a quintessence to transmigrate. Transmigration is a *nonlocal, supraluminal* event occurring when our conscious energy is in negative time-space.

The theory of reincarnation, given the immutable laws of energy transference and worldwide reports of near death experiences, is an extremely convincing doctrine. It seems more believable than any belief which justifies an arbitrary irredemption after death. Reincarnation also helps to explain the seemingly diametrically opposed talents of children within one family. We are all familiar with examples of a child has a natural penchant for art or music, easily absorbing teaching in this area and immediately excelling. Think of 'child prodigies' who excel in certain areas without the benefit of any instruction.

Conversely, think of all the stories of youngsters of aristocratic families who are provided with the most advanced and finest education possible and still are not able to excel.

Consider this comparison. A brother and sister, with the same parents, are raised in the same environment. One becomes a brilliant scholar with fine manners; the other is a dull-headed ragamuffin. What made the difference? The theory of transmigration alone might account for the divergence.

In fact, you may experience memory remnants of reincarnation and not even realize it. Déjà vu, that feeling we experience when we find ourselves having been some place before. This sensation can range from a glimmering sense of recognition to an overpowering feeling of familiarity. The same experience can occur with people, food preferences, or an intense interest in a certain historical period of culture. A person's natural talent in music, art, science, sport, healing, and other activities could also be signs of a possible carryover influence from past lives.

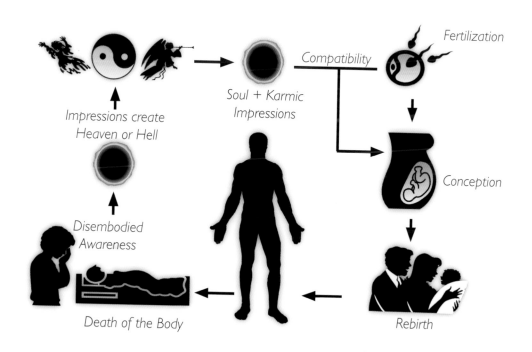

The signs of reincarnation are everywhere. The universe provides us with signals of lives lived previously which are within our personalities, our experiences with other people (ever met someone who you immediately bonded with?), in our dreams, and in the deepest recesses of our minds.

Between death and rebirth, it is unfolding of the memory or the thought content within the subtle and causal plane, which creates a 'heaven' or 'hell' for the departed soul. There is no physical existence of heaven or hell – each is merely a state of mind. Heaven and hell are the dream-like states in which the mind unfolds upon itself. It is the carried-over karmic content, which creates these illusory states. After all, mankind has explored the galaxies and has not heard angelic music yet and fathomed the deep seas only to discover oil!

All our experiences from all of our past lives are contained within the subtle body. Our durable subtle body possesses timeless, spaceless circles of indestructible energy. Through our thoughts, actions, and behavior, we can either fortify or nourish these vortices of inner intelligence or we can starve and contaminate this information that is carried over.

The direction or vector of the transmigrating body is determined by the total algebraic sum of all present and past experiences. The kind of compatible 'fertilized field' that it enters for its next reincarnation will depend on the quality of its contents. *'He attains a fully developed human body in the womb of the mother which is fit for experiencing the fruits of the remainder of works.' Chandogya Upanishad*

This explains the 'circle of life.' Ultimately we are influenced by our previous subliminal impressions – our memories – contained in our disembodied awareness – carried over from one life cycle to the next. This awareness, or potential energy, is an ever-evolving continuum.

The subliminal impressions or *vasanas*, are transmitted through the subtle energy fields surrounding our physical body throughout our life. These energy fields, in turn, are the vehicles for our karmic memories that travel from one lifetime to the next with us. The cycle of *samsara*, or transmigration, is powerfully depicted in one of the *Yoga Upanishads*. The passage symbolizes the cosmic wheel in motion, the uninterrupted chain of deaths and rebirths:

It is happy, the child that sucks
at its mother's breast;
it is the same breast it
fed from in a former life!
The husband takes pleasure
in his wife's belly
he was conceived in the past!
He who was the father
is today the son
and that son, when tomorrow comes,
will be a father in his turn;
thus in the flow of samsara
men are like the buckets
around a water wheel!

Evidence grows in support of reincarnation: Children who remember past lives. People recalling near death experiences or under hypnosis are able to recall their past lives as well as discoveries from 2,500 years of psychospiritual practices in Buddhism and Hinduism. A scientist who fails to examine this information is adopting a dogmatic stance based on faith rather than evidence.

Is it not strange that the learned and the fool equally suffer the pangs of the fear of death. Each one wishes: 'May I not cease to be.' This fear is a natural reaction hidden within our memory of the death of our last body in a previous incarnation.

Transmigration

Man appears as a being whose primary level of existence is at non-space, non-time levels of the Universe, and who has placed himself in a space-time vehicle of consciousness for the purpose of growing in awareness of the True Self.

- William Tiller, Healers and the Healing Process

The subtle body throws off it physical form when the corporeal body has outlived its usefulness. When the subtle body can gather no more relevant experiences in a particular set of circumstances, then the subtle body effectively divorces the corporeal façade. This is what we call death.

At this moment, our senses become incapacitated. We lose our sense of sight, hearing, smell taste and feeling. The power of perception – the pranic vitality – in the sense organs withdraws.

But what happens to the subtle body? Does it die as well? No. The subtle body merely 'moves on'. It gathers into itself all potentials for the faculties, the senses, the mind, the intellect, but not in a physical or material way.

Just as the wind gathers scents from flowers and then wafts them throughout the air, so our subtle body gathers all that we have thought, felt, and lived. Once the material body has died, the ego center remains whole, albeit in another form. The ego lasts as an 'idea', until it comes again to make amends with another form. This 'floating ego' chooses its next physical body based on the total 'reaping' it needs to make within its new form and its overall circumstances.

This is the law of karma. There is no philosophical concept as solid or true as this one. This potent law, if understood fully and properly – actually places the privilege of carving out our own destiny.

Life Before Life

By me thousands of wombs have been seen; various foods have been tasted; and innumerable times mother's milk has been drunk. I have born and died again and again. All my near an dear, for whom I performed various actions, whether good or bad, have enjoyed the benefits of my actions and have left me alone. Once I come out of this birth canal, I am going to surrender myself and contemplate on the Supreme Absolute.

– Garbha Upanishad, 500 B.C.

This excerpt from The *Upanishad* reveals human consciousness while it still resides in the *garbha* or womb. During the final month, the fetus's development is complete; its mind is filled with the memories of past lives. It also completely understands that it is about to incarnate yet again and undergo the obstacles and trials of a physical life form.

All those memories are erased the moment the baby leaves the warmth and protection of the birth canal. Once the infant's delivery system of its life force (*prana*) changes from fluid (inside the womb) to air (outside the womb), all memory vanishes and the individual starts anew, the *Upanishad* tells us.

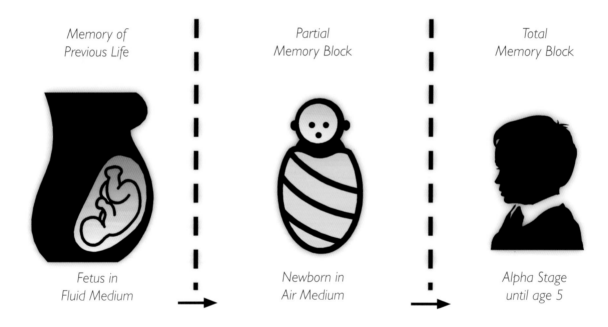

Memory of Previous Life	Partial Memory Block	Total Memory Block
Fetus in Fluid Medium	Newborn in Air Medium	Alpha Stage until age 5

The ancient Vedic Seers' ability to visualize and understand these unseen secrets of the mind, body and soul is truly awesome. Even more stunning is that aspects of scientific research have already confirmed much of these ancient sacred teachings.

Reincarnation is as much a fabric of the lives of many Eastern cultures – especially the Buddhists and Hindus – as is the sunrise and sunset. Mystics have revealed reincarnation throughout the centuries and have never doubted its existence. The Egyptians also believed in life after death. The process of mummification, preparation of the corpse, and the elaborate structures of the pyramids are all evidence of their beliefs.

Even the great ancient Greek philosophers were convinced of life before life ... and life after death. Pythagoras, the great Greek mathematician and philosopher, perhaps most widely known for his theorem on the hypotenuse of the triangle, taught reincarnation in his school. But he wasn't alone. Plato, Aristotle, and Socrates, not to mention a whole host of other philosophers spoke of it, wrote about it – even taught reincarnation to their students.

Roman historians, likewise, accepted the idea of multiple lifetimes, most notably Virgil and Ovid. Josephus, the Roman historian and chronicler, observed that the Jews of his times believed in reincarnation. He noted that in Solomon's Book of Wisdom it says, 'To be born in a sound body with sound limbs is a reward of the virtues of the past lives.'

In the Islamic tradition, Jalaluddin Rumi said, 'I died out of the stone and became a plant; I died out of the plant and became an animal; I died out of an animal and became a man. Why should I fear to die? When did I grow less by dying? I shall die out of a man and become an angel!'

Even early Christian writings contain references to reincarnation, that is, until Emperor Constantine censored them. Constantine, who converted personally to Christianity and thereafter converted the entire Roman Empire to the religion, felt the idea of reincarnation, threatened the stability of the political realm. Those who believed in that doctrine believed they would be given another chance, albeit in a different life at a different time. This, he feared, might be just enough incentive to be less obedient and law-abiding than those who feared the wrath of a single Judgment Day.

The Second Council of Constantinople, convened in the sixth century, underscored the emperor's fears by officially declaring reincarnation to be a heresy. But some refused to go along. Independent thinkers like Origen, Clement of Alexandria and St. Jerome never rejected reincarnation. Neither did the Gnostics.

Lest you think that all Western philosophers ignored or disbelieved this ancient concept consider the number of cogent thinkers who embraced it. They include such great minds as Goethe, Fichte, Schilling and Lessing. Even such recent philosophers as Hume, Spencer and Max Muller have recognized and accepted this doctrine.

Many of us cannot believe that some children between the ages of three to five not only remember a previous life but recognize loved ones from it. We need not 'discover' this concept. Our belief or disbelief in it does not change its existence. Columbus, after all, really did not 'discover' the land which came to be called America – it was all along. More importantly, there has been no evidence to *disprove* the theory of reincarnation.

Without a doubt, the greatest source of evidence for reincarnation comes from scientific research. Dr. Ian Stevenson, a professor of psychiatry at the University of Virginia Medical School, spent 40 years studying this phenomenon. In this time, he has collected more than 3,000 cases involving children from all over the world who have retained memories of past lives.

Even skeptics agree this work, which contains literally hundreds of pictures of documentary evidence, is the best support yet for reincarnation. In many instances, a person's previous past life experiences show up in a physical form during the next life. For example, a boy who had shot himself in the head in a previous life had possessed, since birth, two scars. These lined up perfectly with the placement of the entry and exit wounds in his former life.

Another boy had a red mark across his neck. He remembered his throat had been slit in a previous life. And yet another youngster had a birthmark resembling a surgical scar. It was in the exact location where he had said he had undergone surgery in a previous lifetime.

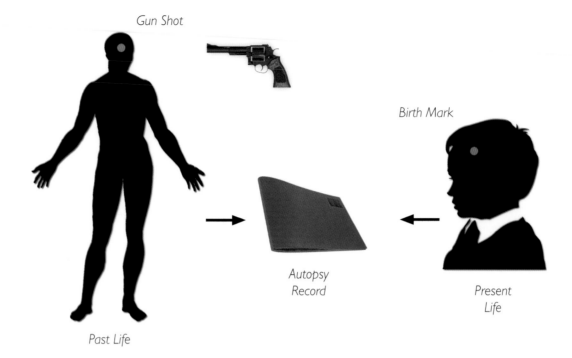

Gun Shot

Birth Mark

Autopsy
Record

Present
Life

Past Life

In many of these cases, Dr. Stevenson obtained hospital autopsy records of the deceased persons these children claimed to have been. He successfully correlated the location of the present birthmarks, scars or other injuries with the past events. Most of these cases are not explained away through genetic factors, infections or other causes currently known to science. The overall reaction of the medical profession, though, is to write these examples off as either anomalies or mere chance.

But Dr. Stevenson has at least offered a preliminary hypothesis. He believes the energy field, acting as a holographic template, carries information from past lives on an 'extended body' or psychophore. In this way, the information is easily transferred from one life to the next.

It is not unusual for the memories of past lives to stay with an individual until the age of five. Theses memories help to explain why children accurately describe former life experiences. Interestingly enough, scientific research shows that *alpha* brain waves are the dominant wave in a child until the age of five. After that they change to *beta* waves.

During his research, Stevenson discovered that it didn't matter whether the children were born into a culture which believed in reincarnation. They possessed these memories whether the culture they lived in accepted it or not.

Carol Brown discovered this same fact and recorded her findings in the book *Children's Past Lives*. Other vigorous investigators of reincarnation include Prof. C.J. Ducasse of Brown University and a team from Duke University who have stacked up an impressive piece of extra-sensory perception data – all pointing to the fact that reincarnation is a very real fact of life. Very few persons – scientists or lay persons – even know about this research, let alone realize it's available for examination.

Dr. Brian Weiss, in his book *Many Lives, Many Masters*, used a tool called hypnotic regression to break the barriers of conventional psychotherapy. Since then, hypnotic regression is a standard – and highly effective – treatment.

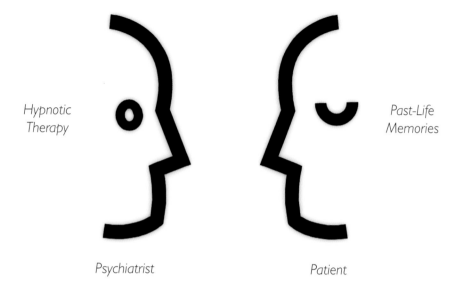

Hypnotic Therapy — Psychiatrist

Past-Life Memories — Patient

Consider Dr. Weiss's work with Catherine, a young patient suffering from a plethora of problems: constant anxiety, panic attacks, phobias, nightmares, insomnia. Conventional therapy failed to help Catherine. Hypnosis, though, proved beneficial.

During treatment, Catherine entered a trance-like state and recalled her former lives. Dr. Weiss recorded these sessions. While in the trance this young woman spoke a foreign language to which she had never before been exposed. This ability is called *xenoglossy*. She recalled past-live memories which contributed to her problems in her present life.

From the 'space between lives', young Catherine acted as a conduit for information that revealed the secret wisdom of life and death. She provided accounts of living numerous lives all over this planet and throughout many eras in history from prehistoric times to ancient Egypt to the twentieth century.

In a matter of only a few sessions, Catherine's symptoms cleared. She resumed her life – free from the anxiety, pain and other problems that had plagued her. Not only did these experiences change Catherine, but they transformed Dr. Weiss's outlook on reincarnation. His findings – which found popularity through his books and public appearances – not only confirm much of what the ancient mystics have told us, it has also provided a new approach to healing.

Emperor Constantine

Emperor Constantine (c.272-337) is best remembered in modern times for the Edict of Milan in 313 and the Council of Nicaea in 325, which fully legalized and then legitimized Christianity in the Roman Empire for the first time. His reputation as the 'first Christian Emperor' has been promulgated by historians from Lactantius and Eusebius of Caesarea to the present day.

Ian Stevenson

Ian Stevenson, MD is Director, of the Division of Personality Studies and Carlson Professor of Psychiatry, at the Department of Psychiatric Medicine, University of Virginia, Charlottesville, Virginia. He is the pre-eminent researcher in the study of reincarnation as well as being the leading scientist studying children who claim to remember previous lives.

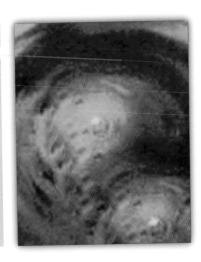

Brian Weiss

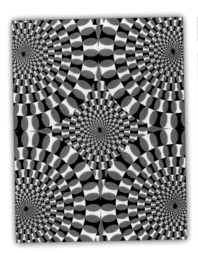

Brian Weiss, MD is a graduate of Columbia University and Yale Medical School and is Chairman Emeritus of Psychiatry at the Mount Sinai Medical Center in Miami. He is the author of several best selling books based on his experience as a psychiatrist and healer.

Fact of Lives

Mr. Hill, the South American explorer, tells the Editor of the 'People' of his experiences: 'I had a strong belief that certain parts of South America were familiar to me. I had a recurring dream that I was an explorer wandering alone in a tropical forest when suddenly a band of dark-skinned men appeared to whom I spoke in their tongue. But for some reason they became angry and their leaders struck me. Eventually I became a steward in the Royal Mail Liners and went to South America. There, I found myself anticipating the names of obscure streets and buildings with accuracy, and I felt as I made my way about Rio de Janeiro, Santos and Buenos Aires that I had surely walked there before. On one voyage we took on board a Danish author at Santos. One day he sent for me to come to his cabin, and said: 'Steward, you are the victim of a remarkable coincidence or something far stranger.'

'Then he showed me a human head taken by him from the head-hunters of Amazon, reduced by a secret process to half of its normal size and preserved. I shuddered. I know I was looking at an exact counterpart of my own face.'

Soldier Castor, the Burmese speaker-George Castor, related some of his past experiences in the Sunday Express, London, (1935). He was a soldier born in 1889. From his boyhood he was speaking while asleep in Burmese. In 1907 he joined the army. In 1909 when he was 20, he was transferred to Maymyo (Burma). While there he felt that he had seen the land, lived in it, and spoken the Burmese tongue. This is an example of xenoglossy. He told Lance Corporal Carrigon that on the other side of the Irrawaddy, there was a large temple with a huge crack in the wall from top to bottom and nearby a large bell-- a statement that was found true to the letter.

An 18 year old boy of Jhamapukhur (Calcutta) was on his death-bed. The boy's parents had thrown themselves at the feet of a Sadhu (ascetic) Purusha. At the same time, they had searched for other means for the boy's cure. The aunt of the boy blamed the Sadhu Purusha saying that faith in the Sadhu was killing him. At this the boy cried out:

'The Sadhu is not to blame. You could not put your trust in him. What has befallen me is nothing when my past Karma is considered. A thousand times more should I suffer. In my past life, I worked in a Railway office and murdered a person, I cut him to pieces. Oh! how I pained him. Where will that Karma go?

'All this happened about 50 years ago when the Suke Street Thana (Police Station) was in charge of a reputed officer who was known as 'Kana' sergeant as he was blind in one eye. He succeeded in arresting me, I escaped the gallows but got hard labor.'

The boy said: 'Mother, I am going now. Do you know why? The person who is sleeping in the other room (referring to his father) was my son in my last birth. He did all he could to make me miserable. To make him feel the consequence of his past Karma I am now born as his son. He must now himself feel the pain and sorrow a son can inflict on his father. Karma can never be evaded and must always be endured.' (Investigation showed that Suke Street Police Station was actually in charge of an officer who was famous all over the city as the blind sergeant and who retired about 50 years ago.)

In 1933, a 18-year-old Hungarian daughter of an engineer lay on her death-bed at Budapest. She escaped death but when she recovered spoke only Spanish and had apparently forgotten her native Hungarian. She could not even recognize her parents whom she referred to as: 'These nice people here are very kind to me, but they are not my parents as they pretend to be.' Speaking to a Spanish interpreter, she said: 'I am Senore Lucid Attarezde Salvio. I was the wife of a working man in Madrid and had 14 children. I was 40 years old and rather sick. A few years ago I died, at least thought I was dying. Now I have recovered in this strange country.'

She sang Spanish songs, prepared special Spanish food, and gave graphic descriptions of Madrid where she had never been.

Life After Life

At age four, this child prodigy wrote sonnets and played the piano in public. At five, he composed his first concerto. And at age seven, he composed his first opera.

That is the raw genius of a young Wolfgang Amadeus Mozart. His immense innate talent appears unexplainable to us Westerners. However, to a culture that accepts the concept of the continuity of the embodied soul, Mozart's seemingly accidental musical abilities are instead viewed as very purposeful.

Soon, Western culture will be compelled to look at the evidence objectively. We cannot continue to ignore irregularities such as child prodigies as mere 'chance.' An uncompromising, true intellectual quest to understand life cannot be fulfilled if it is thwarted at every step of the way by these 'observed irregularities.'

Many claim they don't believe in reincarnation despite the fact that evidence is staring in the face at them. However, their belief or disbelief does not change the existence of life after life. The word 'belief' is used only when there is a lack of validation for a fact. You may say that you don't believe in gravity, for example, yet you are still living under its influence. A distorted belief is dangerous to your life perspective. No explanation is necessary for those who understand, no explanation is possible for those who don't. Believe it or not, the circle of life continues.

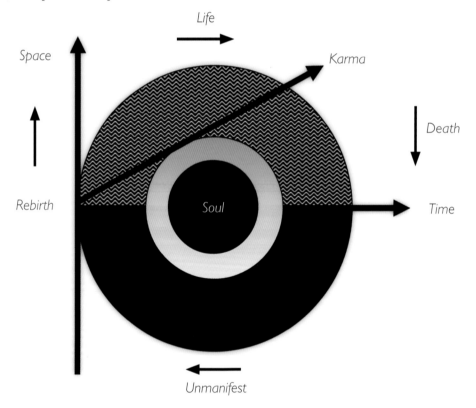

The soul – or *Atman* – comes from *Brahman* and then forgets where it comes from. This is the most common view of the Hindus. The soul in its visit on this plane needs to learn, through a series of lives, that the material world is but an illusion. Then the soul must learn to detach itself from the world and release its karma (total collective impressions) to become increasingly purified and spiritual. Then the *Atman* can finally obtain release from the cycle of birth and death or *moksha* and then rejoin *Brahman*. This cycle mirrors that which is found in the Macrocosm, where the Big Bang is followed by the Big Crunch.

In Buddhism, the concept is *anatta*. Personality characteristics, dispositions and tendencies are carried over. Though the personality itself is discontinued. Each life, according to *anatta*, is lit from the life before it, as a candle takes its flame and lights another. Achieving *nirvana* is similar then to putting out a flame. In fact, *nirvana* means 'blown out.' The Buddha, himself, does not achieve *nirvana*. His mission is to enlighten others.

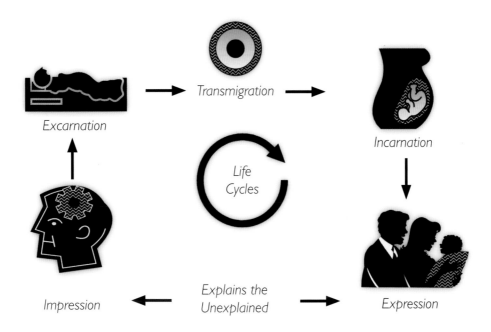

Death is ex-carnation – exiting the physical body when your soul has accomplished its purpose. Then it will find a new home via the *supraluminal, nonlocal* transmigration. The next phase is called re-incarnation (coming into a new physical body) and takes three elements to manifest. The carried over and acquired impressions – nature plus nurture – result in expression. This new expression of life results in the gathering of more impressions. The circle of life remains unbroken.

Blueprint
of Life

Molecule of Life

There are ten trillion individual cells in the human body. To give you an idea of how large a number that is – one trillion is a thousand, thousand million or one thousand billion! Multiply that by ten! About 100,000 of these cells divide every second and each one has about 30,000 genes.

Each of theses 10 trillion cells originated from just one cell: the fertilized egg. The largest of our cells are about the size of a human hair. Most, however, are smaller than that – about one-tenth the diameter of a hair.

Our body cells are organized into tissue, skin, muscle and bone. Each cell contains all of the body's genetic instructions which are stored as DNA – deoxyribonucleic acid. This very long DNA molecule is wound tightly and packaged as chromosomes found in the nucleus of each cell.

We, as humans, have two sets of 23 chromosomes in each cell – 46 in all --one set of which we inherited from each parent. One set – X and Y – determines the sex. Another set contains a copy of each of the roughly 30,000 genes in the human 'genome', the term used to refer to the complete genetic instructions for an organism. This extremely long DNA molecule is actually composed of a long string of chemical building blocks called 'nucleotides.' There are four different nucleotides labeled adenine (A), thymine (T), guanine (G) and cytosine (C). The human genome is made of a sequence of roughly three billion of these nucleotides.

Each DNA molecule in a single cell is about 1.7 meters and wound tightly round itself. If all the DNA in the body were stretched, it would reach the Moon and back 6,000 times. Each DNA molecule that forms a chromosome can also be seen as a set of shorter DNA sequences. The fundamental units of its function are what we call genes. They guide the production of one particular component of an organism.

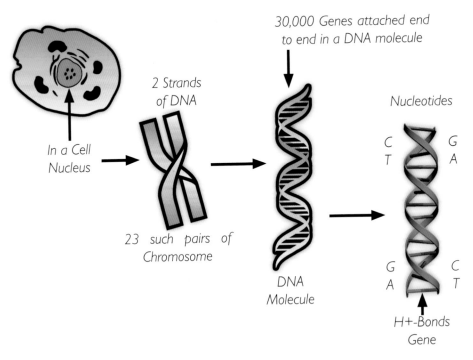

In a Cell Nucleus

2 Strands of DNA

23 such pairs of Chromosome

30,000 Genes attached end to end in a DNA molecule

DNA Molecule

Nucleotides

C
T

G
A

G
A

C
T

H+-Bonds
Gene

The DNA within the nucleus of the cell encodes the structural-physical expression of the cell's activities. But the DNA is only an informational manual containing instructions. We still need a few intermediate actors in the cellular scheme of things to activate this material.

These actors are called enzymes, the protein-bodied workers that carry out the myriad of every day biomedical tasks. The enzymes catalyze specific reactions of chemicals, either to create structure through molecular assemblies or to ignite the electrochemical fire needed to run the cellular engines. These vital functions ultimately keep the entire system working efficiently.

Enzymes – which are composed of proteins – are actually collections of amino acids strung together in a linear array like colored beads on a thread. The positive and negative charges of the amino acids, through the natural laws of electrostatic attraction and repulsion – cause this string of beads to 'self-assemble' into a functional three-dimensional structure.

The 'active' site – located in the center of this macromolecule – is the area where the chemical reactions are catalyzed. The DNA molecule encodes and then assigns the sequential arrangement of various 'colored' amino acids from each type of protein in its genetic structural memory.

Watson, Crick and Wilkins

In 1962 Watson, Crick and Wilkins received the Nobel Prize in Medicine for proposing that the DNA molecule takes the shape of a double helix, an elegantly simple structure that resembles a gently twisted ladder.

Francis Crick tells the story of how he went to dinner with James Watson at a club for scientists in England, and when people asked about the structure of DNA, all Watson could do – inspired by little too much wine -- was repeat that it was beautiful.

Of Mice and Men

Remarkably, mice and humans share a set of genes that are almost identical. In fact, the similarities are so close that the mouse is often used as a scientific tool to promote the advancement of medicine for humans.

Almost every gene found in the human being has been found in the mouse as well in a closely related form. Of the 4,000 genes studied so far, scientists have found less than 10 percent that are not common.

Both mouse and human genomes contain about 30,000 genes, 3,000 million bases and 3.1 million base pairs or chemical letters. Of the total sequence, only about 5 percent is composed of protein-coding regions or genes. More than 90 percent is non-coding DNA – sometimes referred to as 'junk' because we have yet to determine what function it performs.

Common ancestor
80 million years ago

90%
identical
Gene to gene

30,000 genes
3000 million bases
3.1 million base pairs
46 chromosomes

30,000 genes
3000 million bases
3.1 million base pairs
40 chromosomes

This large amount of non-coding DNA makes it very hard to recognize the genes and regulatory regions within this molecule. Many scientists call them the 'switches' that are responsible for turning the gene expressions on or off, up or down. They exist as poorly defined 'consensus' sequences.

The protein-coding regions of the mouse and human genomes are, in fact, nearly 90 percent the same. It is these regions that are conserved through the evolutionary process because they are vital for the proper functioning of organisms.

By contrast, the areas not used for coding are more diverse – less than 50 percent of this material is the same. This makes the similarity of the functional elements even more outstanding.

The human and mouse – as well as other mammals – shared a common ancestor nearly 80 million years ago. It should come as no surprise then that genetic material of all mammals is very closely related. The closer an animal is related to humans on the evolutionary chain, the more closely the genetic material mirrors the other. The genome of humans and our closest relatives, the apes, bear a 98 percent resemblance.

Cell Differentiation

Each cell starts as an entity that can grow to perform any function. As the body develops and more cells grow, the cell transforms from unspecialized stem cells to highly specialized ones. This is called cell differentiation and it's what prompts changes in both the physical and functional properties of the body.

Each cell carries the same genetic library of instructions – DNA – but as the cells mature, they only read the chapters pertaining to their function. This selective reading process – or organizational knowledge – ensures all the body's features will function properly. Cell differentiation is an 'exact science'. If any one gene is missed, read out of sequence or altered in any way, the cell differentiation of the living organism changes dramatically.

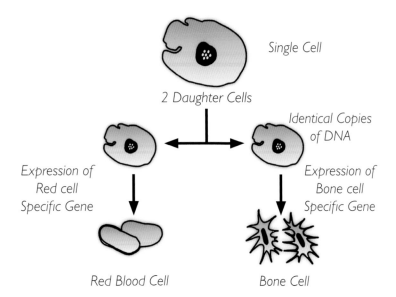

Single Cell

2 Daughter Cells

Identical Copies of DNA

Expression of Red cell Specific Gene

Expression of Bone cell Specific Gene

Red Blood Cell

Bone Cell

The timing of this process depends on the stage of the embryo's development as well as the location of the cell. Cells destined eventually to be part of the eye, for example, use different combinations of genes than do brain or skin cells.

What triggers cell differentiation? Scientists are still working at unlocking that part of nature's hidden secrets. For example, researchers know for sure that the genes control the internal signals of the cells. Chemicals in the micro-environment and physical contact with neighboring cells are some of the external signals that dictate cell performance.

Cloning can be thought of a technological virgin birth. Prior to cell differentiation, any cell is able to create an entire living creature. To clone a frog, for example, DNA material from a fertilized frog's egg is removed and exchanged for DNA from an adult frog's intestinal cell. Since each cell contains the same library of information found in every other cell, it makes it possible to produce a completely identical frog without sexual reproduction.

A fertilized egg in a supportive environment expresses the full potential of the genetic blueprint. The holographic principle is mirrored in us through our cells: Each cell contains the information of the whole, just like each unit of the holographic apple carries the entire image of the apple.

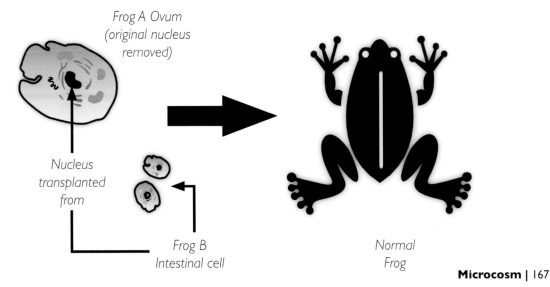

Frog A Ovum
(original nucleus removed)

Nucleus transplanted from

Frog B
Intestinal cell

Normal
Frog

Gene Expression

While scientists still don't quite understand how cells differentiate, they are beginning to unlock the keys of how genes express themselves. The human body taps into its inherent intelligence to make one of the most important building blocks of its system: proteins. Their formation is controlled by a sequence of genes, called structural genes, located in a series on the same chromosomal DNA strand. This area of the DNA is called the operon.

An additional band of nucleotides consists of a repressor and an activator operator, which turn the transcription process off and on. The operon controls the regulatory gene. This prompts the formation of a regulatory protein that acts either as an activator or as a repressor on the operon, much like a light switch controls the flow of electricity to a light bulb.

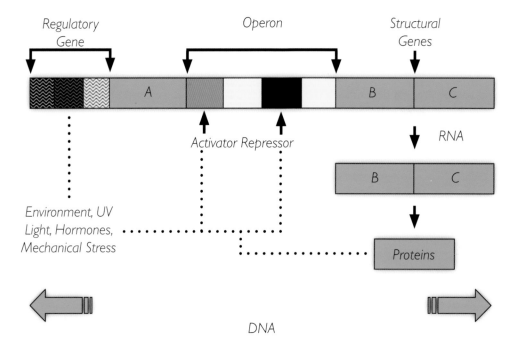

The presence of a specific amount of synthesized protein in the cell can cause negative feedback inhibition of the operon. Simply put, when there is enough of the required product for proper cell formation, the operon then turns dormant.

Conversely, once the synthesized product degrades in the cell and its concentration decreases, the operon activates. Occasionally other external signals, like hormones or environmental factors, control these chemical reactions.

Cells use this two-step process of transcription and translation to read genes and produce the string of amino acids that make up a protein.

The genetic code is transcribed from the genes into a single strand of the Ribonucleic Acid (RNA) molecule. Then the process of translation sends the information from the RNA into the proteins. RNA works much like a disposable version of DNA – similar to the copies of our reference book. It is good for a single, specific function, but not for the storage of information.

Karmic Impression

Every human being shares the same genetic material. Each of us carries, the same genes as our neighbor, yet miraculously no two of us are exactly identical. These differences result from tiny changes in our DNA sequences. The effects can, indeed, be large depending upon their placement in the genome.

Growth and development of our physical body, from its beginnings as an embryo and on into adulthood are influenced by genetic patterns. However, that is *not* the only influence shaping our individuality. We are also shaped by holographic karmic impressions which affect the regulatory gene and continue to influence the patterns of cellular expression. Unlike genetic traits this is not a random phenomenon.

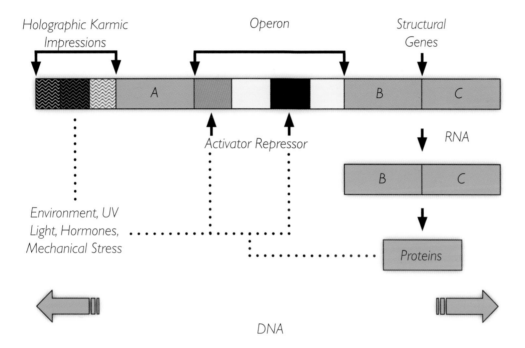

What awesome power is that which governs the gene? You'll remember that 90 percent of our genome is non-coding DNA, which has at this time no known function. Communicating through quantum intelligence, 'karmic impression' is the unseen force, which acts on this so-called 'nonfunctional' DNA, which in turn affects the gene regulatory activity. *The gene, then, is not the cause … but the effect.*

The fascinating story of development is long and intricate. It involves a blending of the genetic pool and karmic transmigration. The compatibility between the parental genetic material and the karmic impression carried over is not only specific, but it dictates entry into the womb. One chooses one's parents and the parents choose the one. And as a result of this trio of influences, both the physical and mental attributes of the offspring are never the perfect algebraic sum of the mother and the father.

For example, if you were to take a photograph of a mother and a father and superimpose them on a computer, then you should be able to predict with some accuracy what their offspring would look like. But you can't. The child is more than just the algebraic sum of his parents' physical features. There is always the unrecognized, carried over third element at work.

Microcosm | 169

Karma-Gene Link

Genetic memory requires the unbroken passage of genetic material throughout the generations. Memories of past lives, though, do not follow a genetic trail. People recall lives from all eras, and all regions of the world, which would imply multiple genetic histories. No genetic line is followed; in fact, it is repeatedly disrupted.

How, then, can these memories be recalled from one life to the next with no single source of genetic material from which to pull?

The story of its development is both fascinating and complicated. Its telling belongs to both the correlation of the genetic pool and karmic transmigration. The compatibility between the parental genetic impressions and the carried-over karmic impressions is indeed extremely specific and dictates entry into the womb.

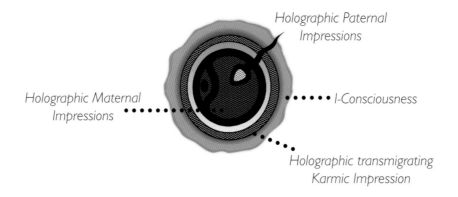

The third element is evident from the moment the sperm meets the egg. The fertilized ovum contains all that is physically necessary for the creation of a complete human being; conception is still necessary for its genetic expression and this requires the carried over I-Consciousness. What we can't see is the holographic quintessence of the father's and the mother's thought body uniting with the transmigrating karmic impressions.

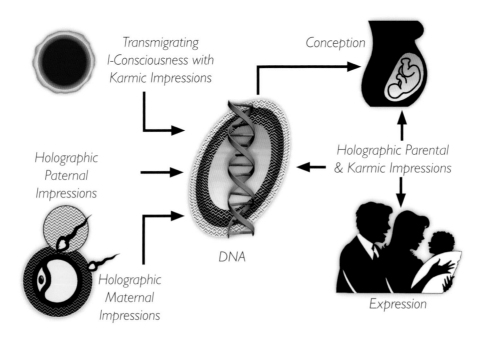

Therefore, the physical and mental characteristics of the offspring can never be fully attributed to the perfect algebraic sum of the mother and the father. There is always a third element that influences the development. There is a third element even in the creation of homozygous twins – who share the same DNA and come from the same egg. These siblings, identical in so many ways, are also unique individuals whose mannerisms, likes, and dislikes are noted by those closest to them. Therefore, it is hard not to believe that a third element is at work here.

As a species we share the same genes. But the way they are arranged varies with each person and that is what separates us as individuals. Even though the DNA of any two people is the same, it is the *unseen* karmic impressions that express our individuality. We additionally are products of our environment, or our nurturing. The karmic impressions are our *nature*, whereas our interaction with the environment is our *nurture*.

Scientists are finally seeing that the differences in genes among species are really very minimal. The basic organization of life is shared among all living creatures. The greatest genetic differences are not found between the mammals, but are seen between the plant and animal worlds and between the single-celled organism like yeast and the large multi-cellular organisms such as ourselves.

The karmic gene link explains what scientists have failed to uncover: It is evident from examining the similarities of the genomes that a seemingly small difference in the gene makes a large difference in its expression.

Impression-DNA Transfer

The discovery of DNA heralded a new and exciting era in scientific research. It opened doors to greater learning; it allowed us to peak inside our cells and get a better understanding of what exactly makes us the biological creatures we are.

While our knowledge of our genetic workings has grown immensely, there are still a myriad of questions that remain unanswered. Scientists know that the now familiar double helix shape of the DNA holds a blueprint of the body's protein and amino acids. They also know that the complete DNA molecule is found in each and every one in our body's 10 trillion cells.

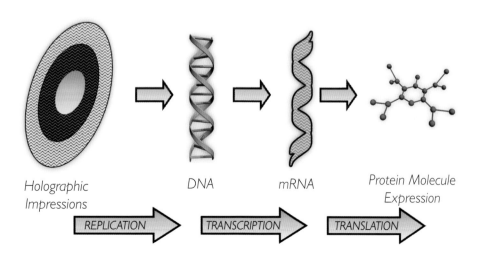

Holographic Impressions DNA mRNA Protein Molecule Expression

REPLICATION TRANSCRIPTION TRANSLATION

They certainly know that DNA directs the building of the body by providing RNA with specific information to trigger a chain reaction of activity. DNA gives a specific set of directions to the RNA molecule, which then passes the information on to the amino acids. This group of amino acids is then able to create proteins. These proteins, in turn, control the chemical processes inside the cell which ultimately run the body.

However, current scientific knowledge falls short in explaining how DNA knows when to orchestrate all of this. Scientists also do not completely understand how these chemicals, all apparently blindly bumping into each other, can operate efficiently and simultaneously in every one of the body's cells. Each cell undergoes an average of 100,000 chemical reactions every second.

If all of these genes are working together like a symphony orchestra playing a beautiful concerto, then who or what is the conductor?

But what awesome power is that which governs the DNA?

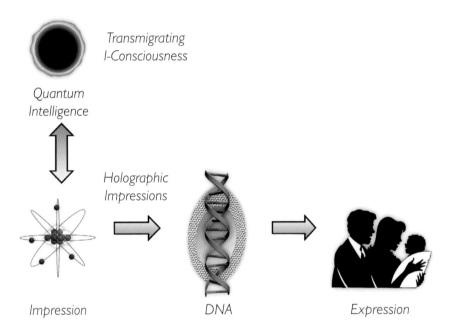

It is consciousness embedded within the holographic karmic and parental impressions, expressed through quantum intelligence which guide the atoms of the DNA molecule. The interference pattern of karmic intelligence is constantly imprinting. It is the blueprint of intelligence.

Impression Memory Transfer

The following experiments help us to better understand the transference of karmic impressions and memories.

Specific molecular signals could be transferred, Jacques Benveniste demonstrated in 1991, by using an amplified, electromagnetic coil. Four years later, he recorded and replayed these signals using a multimedia computer.

Benveniste and his colleague, Guillonet, recorded the activity of the molecule on a computer. They exposed it to a biological system sensitive to that substance. The pair performed these actions literally thousands of times. In each instance, the taped version of molecular activity actually 'fooled' the biological system. It believed – and acted as if – it were interacting with the substance itself, initiating the biological chain reaction as if it were in the presence of the original molecule.

But Benveniste and his team did not stop there. They discovered they could erase theses signals and actually stop the cellular activity through an alternating magnetic field. Performing this important work in collaboration with the Centre National de la Recherché Scientifique in Medudon, France, they arrived at an inescapable, if unorthodox, conclusion. Molecules speak to each other in oscillating frequencies. In fact, it appeared that *molecules speak to each other nonlocally and virtually instantaneously.*

The researchers then tested 'digital biology' on plasma coagulation. Plasma – the yellow liquid portion of blood which carries both protein and waste products, coagulates. To control this, calcium must be removed from the plasma. This process is known as chelation. Then they added water containing calcium to the blood. It coagulated. But when they added heparin, a classic anticoagulant drug, it blocked the blood from clotting even in the presence of the calcium.

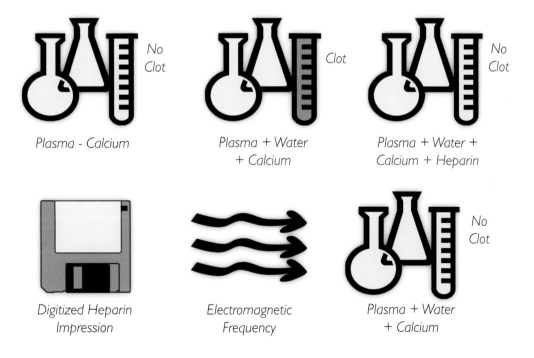

No Clot — *Plasma - Calcium*

Clot — *Plasma + Water + Calcium*

No Clot — *Plasma + Water + Calcium + Heparin*

Digitized Heparin Impression

Electromagnetic Frequency

No Clot — *Plasma + Water + Calcium*

Benveniste then took a test tube of the plasma in which the calcium had been chelated out. To this tube he added water that contained calcium and that had been exposed to the 'sound' of heparin. This 'sound' was transmitted through a signature digitized electromagnetic frequency. Just as in all his other experiments, Benveniste's signature frequency of heparin works as though the molecules of the anti-coagulant drug itself were there. In its presence, the blood is more reluctant than usual to coagulate.

But could the signal, Benveniste asked himself, be sent across space and still have an affect? Colleagues of his at Northwestern University in Chicago recorded signals from four substances: ovalbumin (ova), acetylcholine (ach), dextran, and water. The signals from these molecules were recorded on a transducer and a computer equipped with a sound card. The signal was then transferred to a floppy disk and either sent through regular mail or sent as an attached document in an e-mail to the DigiBio Laboratory in Clamart.

The Clamart team exposed ordinary water to the signals and to isolated guinea pig hearts. All the digitized water produced highly significant changes in coronary flow compared to the controls, which contained non-exposed water.

The effects from the digitized water were identical to effects produced on the heart by the actual substances themselves. If indeed, digital biology explains how digital signatures are transferred in cyberspace, it is not a giant leap to think that karmic impressions could very well transfer in a similar manner.

Memory of Water

Could it be that water 'remembers'?

While certainly not starting out to prove it, Jacques Benveniste, a French medical doctor, stumbled upon the idea that water might retain a 'memory' of substances it once had dissolved.

Benveniste began with basophils, a type of white blood cell, which contains antibodies of immunoglobulin, E (IgE) type on its surface. These cells are responsible for hypersensitivity reactions in people with allergies. These are stained with a standard dye, in this case toluidine blue, in order to be able to see them.

Exposure of IgE cells to anti-IgE antibodies change their ability to absorb the dye. Because of this, they have been nicknamed 'biological paint-stripper.' They can render the basophils invisible again.

Benveniste's team created high dilutions of the anti-IgE by pouring one-tenth of the previous solution into a test tube. Then they filled that tube by adding nine parts of a standard solvent. Each solution was succussed – or vigorously shaken – as if it were being prepared for homeopathic solutions.

The research team continued to use dilutions like these – one part solution to nine parts solvent. Upon each creation, the team kept diluting the mixtures, until the ratio was one part solution to 99 parts solvent. In fact, the researchers took the mixture to such a diluted state of one part solution to 999 parts solvent.

Each of theses highly diluted mixtures was added to the basophil, which was then examined under a microscope. What the team discovered stunned everyone. Even with dilutions of 100 fold, inhibited dye absorption was still recorded. In fact, dye absorption was recorded for solutions as weakened as 10^{120}, where there was absolutely no possibility that a single molecule of the IgE could possibly be left. Yet the basophils were still affected.

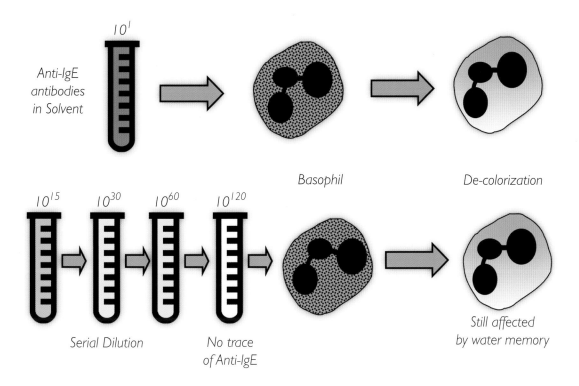

As amazing as these results were, the most stunning revelation was yet to unfold. The effect of the highly diluted IgE began *increasing at the ninth dilution and, in fact, increased as the solution weakened.*

The series of experiments, Benveniste concluded, proved the claim of homeopathy that the weaker the solution, the more powerful its healing effect.

The experiment's results proved so amazing to Benveniste and his team that he joined with 12 other scientists in five different laboratories in four countries – France, Israel, Italy and Canada – to attempt to duplicate the results. Each of these researchers successfully replicated the original outcome. These scientists then jointly published their independently gained results in a single scholarly article in the highly prestigious *Nature* magazine in 1988.

The article stated that since not one of the molecules they used was present in the dilution, the specific information must have been transmitted as part of the 'memory of the water.' The only obvious conclusion, Benveniste and the other professionals agreed, is that water is capable of imprinting and storing information from molecules.

These results directly affect our understanding of how impressions or memories affect the molecules in human cells. After all, seventy percent of our body is water and thirty percent is solid.

Water Expression

Our thoughts and feelings affect physical reality. In fact, our thoughts and feelings can even penetrate physical reality so deeply that they affect the molecular structure of a substance as seemingly innocuous as water.

This thesis is what places Dr. Masaru Emoto at the forefront in the study of water crystallization. Emoto exposes a variety of focused, loving thoughts, using both the written and spoken words as well as music, to samples of water and records the results. His objective is to discover if there are changes in the expression of the water because of these intentions. In other words, do the samples freeze differently if exposed to different thoughts? He also wanted to see if water contaminated by pollution froze any differently than water that was clear and clean.

Using an extremely powerful microscope in a very cold environment, Emoto utilized high speed photography to achieve his goal. He photographed the newly formed crystals of ice on water samples that had been exposed to a variety of loving, caring intentions. He also took samples of water that were exposed to hurtful and harmful thoughts.

Emoto soon discovered that not all the samples crystallized uniformly. Samples of polluted river water did not crystallize at all. If the samples had been exposed to negative thoughts they formed incomplete, asymmetrical patterns that lacked much color.

Water from clear springs, on the other hand,   as well as water which had been exposed to loving words showed complex and colorful snowflake patterns as they crystallized.

Asymmetrical pattern

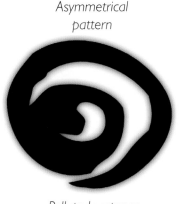

Polluted water or water exposed to negative thoughts

Snowflake pattern

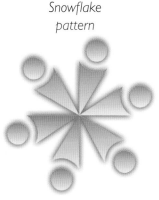

Spring water or water exposed to positive thoughts

What does this research mean for us? If human consciousness does, indeed, *affect* the formation of water crystals, then just imagine how potent an influence is the causal power of consciousness without our even realizing it?

Masaru Emoto

Dr. Masaru Emoto was born in Japan and was a graduate of the Yokohama Municipal University and the Open International University as a Doctor of Alternative Medicine. His photographs were first featured in his self-published books Messages from Water 1 and 2. The Hidden Messages in Water was first published in Japan, with over 400,000 copies sold internationally.

Secrets

- *The Earth is nearly 5 billion years old and human-like creatures emerged some time between six and four million years ago.*

- *The first modern humans evolved in Africa about 100,000 years ago.*

- *Scientists theorize that life sprang from 'non-life' early in Earth's history when a bolt of lightening struck the 'prebiotic soup.'*

- *Others claim there is fossil evidence for the first one-celled life forms.*

- *Matter and energy are actually compatible, interchangeable entities.*

- *Matter is nothing but 'frozen energy' or a specialized energy 'field.'*

- *The body is an extension of mind.*

- *Spirit or Pure Self is self-aware energy ... ever free, ever pure and ever wise.*

- *Only when the Conscious principle ignites the inner core of the Unconscious principle – and the equilibrium is disturbed – do the forces of Nature begin to interact.*

- *It is from the interaction of the three forces of Nature and the two polarities that all objective material phenomenon is produced.*

- *Electro-photography provides evidence of the subtle body.*

- *The energy field that surrounds and penetrates living systems is referred to as the 'subtle body.'*

- *Contained in the subtle body are the ten faculties of perception and action and their psychological correlates, I-Consciousness, intellect, ego and the mind.*

- *Bioenergetic field is divided it into three different levels: instinctive, intellectual and spiritual.*

- *DNA is the molecule responsible for hereditary instructions in the cell.*

- *The nucleotide bases combine to instruct cells how to make specific proteins.*

- *More than 90 percent is non-coding DNA – sometimes referred to as 'junk' DNA.*

- *The genome of humans and our closest relatives, the apes, bear a 98 percent resemblance.*

- *The protein-coding regions of the mouse and human genomes are, in fact, nearly 90 percent the same.*

- *Scientists are still working at unlocking nature's hidden secret of cell differentiation.*

- *The operon controls the regulatory gene.*

- *The gene is not the cause … but the effect.*

- *Genetic memory requires the unbroken passage of genetic material throughout the generations.*

- *There is always a third element that influences embryonic development.*

- *Even though the DNA of any two people is the same, it is the unseen karmic impressions that help express our individuality.*

- *Current scientific knowledge though falls short in explaining how DNA knows how to orchestrate cell differentiation.*

- *Molecules speak to each other nonlocally and virtually instantaneously.*

- *Water is capable of imprinting and storing information from molecules.*

- *Our thoughts and feelings affect physical reality.*

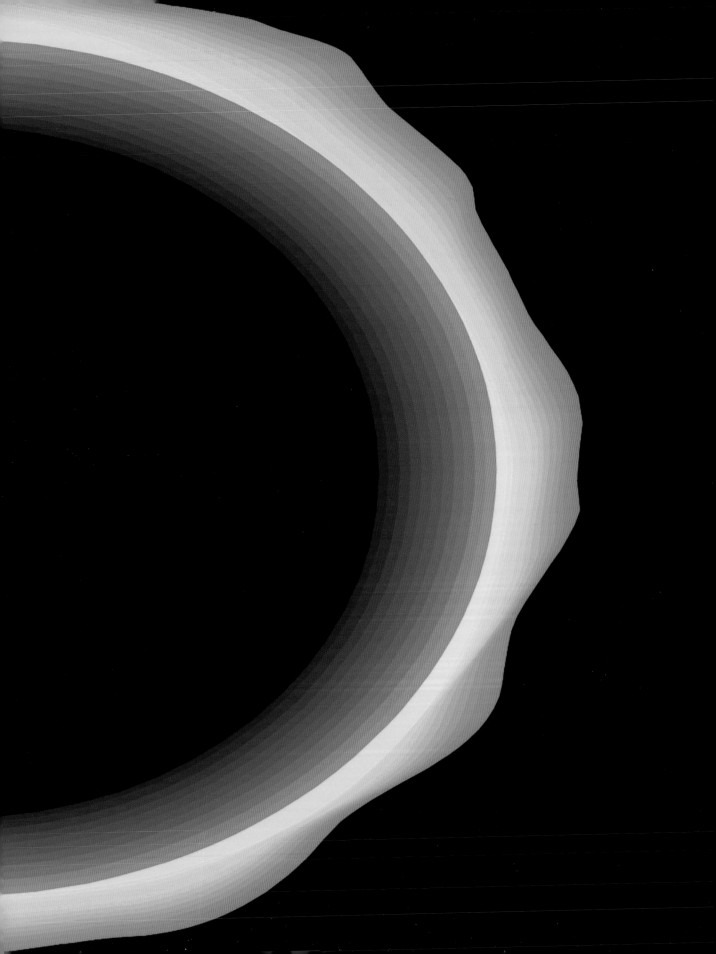

Reality

We have looked at nanocosm, macrocosm, and microcosm to better understand the origin and the structure of the manifest. There is one thing that all of these different paradigms have in common. They are all grounded in eternal consciousness or the True Reality.

Up until now scientists have unknowingly flirted with this illusion failing to realize what the ancient wisdom has always espoused; that Consciousness is the substratum of True Reality.

They have looked at the different aspects of the world as distinct parts, perpetuating the illusion of separateness. But when seen from the viewpoint of the ancient mystics, the illusion is unveiled and one clearly sees 'unity in diversity.' True Reality or Consciousness is the substratum underlying the three '-cosms'.

Self-Aware
Universe

Evolution of Consciousness

Just as the physical body of humans has developed and evolved over its 30,000 to 50,000 year old history, so has our consciousness. Cultural anthropologists believe that consciousness has evolved at even a greater rate than the physical body. Very little in the way of our appearance has changed over the millennia, yet we view and relate to the world and those around us vastly different than we used to. It is expected that our level of awareness will only expand further.

The evolution of our consciousness is occurring on two levels: individually and as a species. Within the species as a whole, in fact, there exists varying degrees of awareness. Itzhak Bentov plotted the quality and quantity of consciousness on a graph. The resulting graph would most certainly resemble a bell curve, with some people far more advanced than others.

Individuals, as they go through reincarnations, generally gain greater awareness. Gradually, humanity as a whole will reach a more advanced perception of Reality and our place within it.

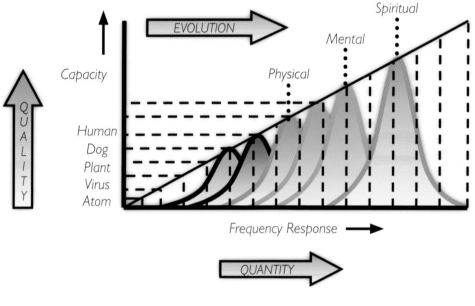

(adapted from I.Bentov)

All of matter – even atoms – contain some degree of consciousness, all of which is evolving to progressively higher planes just as we are. With each new level comes a proportionately higher degree of complexity as well as a fullness of expression that matches that level.

The evolution of human consciousness was envisioned by all spiritual traditions. Some Native American cultures, for example, believe we are currently living under what they call the Fifth Sun of consciousness. Shortly, they say, we will be entering the Sixth Sun and with it will come a fundamental transformation of our world.

Some philosophers have attempted to explain the specific stages of evolution of human awareness. These speculative concepts are as diverse as those who offer them. Some say the next stage will be a 'super consciousness' in some individuals.

While such concepts may be as different as are the terms used to describe them, they all share a common thread. Evolution of human awareness evolves from the ego-bound to the transpersonal form. Transpersonal awareness makes itself more readily accessible to a wider variety of information. In other words, the human mind will be more accepting of new ideas on all subjects – including spirituality and Reality.

This shift in human thinking carries with it the great potential to be a world-changing event. A source of great hope, the transpersonal consciousness could produce individuals who have greater empathy as well as those with greater sensitivity to animals and plants. Such an evolutionary shift could possibly create subtle contact with parts of the cosmos as well.

A society whose consciousness is characterized by a transpersonal awareness would most likely be less materialistic and self-centered. Societies would be, hopefully, more peaceful and sustainable.

Itzhak Bentov

Itzhak Bentov (1923-1979) was born in Czechoslovakia and moved to America. He became an inventor and specialized in the creation of new medical instrumentation. Shortly after writing his book 'Stalking the Wild Pendulum: On the Mechanics of Consciousness', he died in a flying accident. He was an early pioneer in the research of consciousness. By blending analytical knowledge and intuitive insight, he was the first to develop what is now widely accepted as a holographic model of reality.

Nature of Consciousness

The view that consciousness is produced in and by the brain is just one of the many views that have been offered to explain the relationship between the physical brain and the conscious mind. Referred to as the *materialist* way, this idea states that consciousness is a by-product of the brain.

As organisms evolve into more complex creatures, they require a more complex 'computer' to direct them to find food, a mate, and other related resources needed to survive and reproduce. At some given point in the development of the organism, consciousness appears. Synchronized neural firings and transmissions of energy and chemical substances between the synapse produce the qualitative stream of experience that we call consciousness.

The materialist way contends that consciousness is not primary in the world, but rather is an 'epiphenomenon' created by the complex material system we know as the human brain.

But if we are nothing more than material possibilities, how does our observation collapse a quantum wave of possibility? Quantum collapse is a paradox only if the 'materialist way' existed in the world.

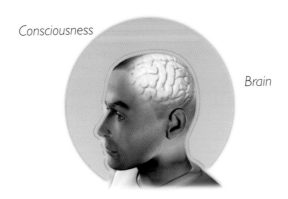

Consciousness

Brain

Our consciousness is essential to the process of subatomic particle actualization. The correct, paradoxical-free way of understanding consciousness is then the *idealist* theory. From this perspective, consciousness is seen as the first and only Reality. Matter is an illusion created by our mind. This is the view of the ancient Vedic masters. Those who understand this explain that we do not experience the world directly, but through our consciousness. We assume that there is a qualitatively different physical world beyond our consciousness, but that may be an illusion.

Everything we experience, the Vedic Masters contend, is actually a part of our consciousness. The material world is merely our creation. The world, in fact, is our attempt to make sense of the flow of sensations in our consciousness.

It is the consciousness that wields the ultimate power: to create manifest Reality by freely choosing among the possibilities offered.

Levels of Consciousness

Sigmund Freud probably did more than any other individual to teach and popularize the idea of human consciousness. His work laid the foundation of how scientists view the brain-mind relationship and opened new vistas to our understanding.

Freud's main contribution to the body of literature on the subject was extensive research concerning the unconscious mind. While he didn't invent the idea of conscious versus unconscious, he popularized it.

Through his work with neurotic patients, this psychoanalyst realized that there existed an unconscious dynamic that worked beneath their conscious actions. While he attempted to use hypnosis to tap into the unconscious, he found this only produced limited results. Instead, he concentrated on analyzing the dreams of his patients, which yielded a wealth of information about an individual's desires and motivations.

Dreams represent wish fulfillment, Freud concluded. Their complex nature, he additionally reasoned, was due to a person's inner censor which made a final attempt to prevent forbidden thoughts from surfacing to the consciousness level.

The conscious mind, according to Freud, is information you are aware of at any given moment. This information includes your present perceptions, memories, thoughts, feelings, and even fantasies. Freud called this part of the human mind the ego. Working closely with the conscious mind is what Freud labeled the preconscious segment of the mind or the superego. This basically is your 'available memory.' It is anything that can easily be made conscious. This includes memories that you are not thinking about at the moment, but which can easily be recalled.

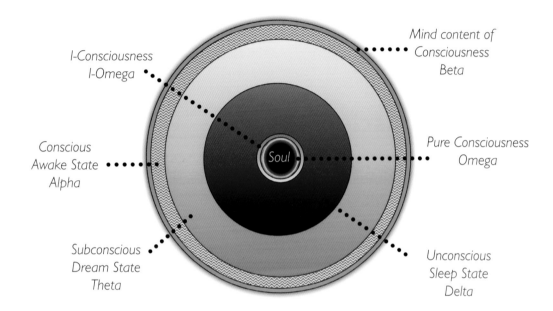

Freud contended that these two parts of the human mind were actually the smallest segments. The largest part, he said, was our unconscious, which he called the id. It includes all things hidden from awareness as well as many thoughts and urges which originate from this source. Embedded within our unconscious minds are our instinctual drives, memories, and emotions. We cannot deal with these at the conscious level.

The unconscious is the source of our motivations, as well, Freud said. Simple desires start at the unconscious level, like those for food or sex, as well as the more complex or higher yearnings, as in the pursuit of art or scientific findings.

In contrast, according to the *Vedas*, the field of 'I' awareness is in close proximity to the pure Self, and along with the unconscious is the expression of the blissful, dreamless sleep state and the realm of meditation. This causal body contains all the carried over and the acquired impressions or *vasanas* in the seed state. They are the source of our thoughts, urges, emotions, desires, and memories.

The unresolved impressions, however, present themselves in the dream state to be processed. The subtle body--the second layer of the human cake--corresponds to the dream state and the subconscious. The dream is made possible by the *light* of consciousness provided by the *Atman* or Pure Self.

What we call the awake consciousness is only the 'tip of the iceberg.' Thoughts arise from the deep-seated *vasanas* and surface to constitute the linear thinking mind.

Sigmund Freud

Sigmund Freud (1856–1939) was an Austrian neurologist and the founder of the psychoanalytic school of psychology. He theorized that human development is best understood in terms of changing objects of sexual desire; that the unconscious often represses wishes and may express themselves in dreams and 'Freudian slips.' These unconscious conflicts are the source of neuroses and could be treated through bringing the unconscious to the conscious in psychoanalytic treatment.

Collective Consciousness

While the traditional model of psychiatry and psychoanalysis is strictly personalistic and biographical, modern consciousness research has added new levels, realms, and dimensions and shows the human psyche as being essentially commensurate with the whole universe and all of existence.

--Stanislav Grof

Consciousness itself provides the perfect example of the holographic model at work. It is no surprise that the field of psychology has been affected by this most surprising scientific idea.

Bohm, who first suggested the model, points to consciousness, in fact, to illustrate his meaning of undivided and flowing movement. While the ebb and flow of our consciousness is not precisely definable, it can still be viewed as a deeper and a more fundamental Reality from which our thoughts and ideas unfold. Consider these entities much as you would the ripples and whirlpools of a fast-moving stream. Some ripples appear and linger for a while; some whirlpools form and persist, self perpetuating themselves and in act, growing larger. And other 'disturbances' in the stream disappear almost as quickly as they came.

The holographic model also provides immeasurable insight into the otherwise unexplainable bonds that occasionally occur in the consciousness of two or more people.

Carl Jung, an eminent Swiss psychiatrist of the early twentieth century, was the first to explore this connection. Early in his career, Jung noted the dreams, artwork, fantasies and even the hallucinations of his patients appeared to contain symbols and ideas that extended far beyond the products of their personal histories. The experiences of his patients more closely resembled images and themes of some of the world's great mythologies and religions. Hallucination, religious visions, dreams, and myths, he concluded, all spring from a single source, a collective unconscious shared by all people.

While Jung's concept is now embraced by untold thousands of professionals in the field of psychology and psychiatry, we still can't explain why it exists. However, if you take into account the holographic model, the answer begins to form. In a universe in which everything is intimately and infinitely connected, all consciousness is also interconnected. Despite the appearance of being separate beings, we are all one without borders. This is very much like the islands in an ocean, which look separate on the surface but are interconnected at the bottom. We are discovering that 'deep down the consciousness of mankind is one' as Bohm originally explained.

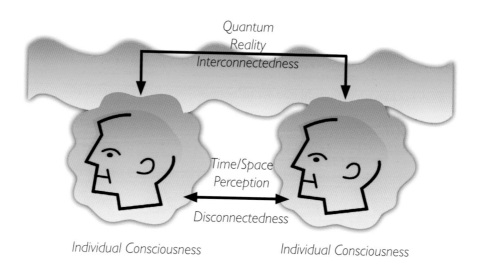

So, if we all have access to the unconscious knowledge of the entire human race, why aren't we all walking encyclopedias? Perhaps it is because we can only tap into information in the implicate order that is directly relevant to our memories. This explanation is offered by psychologist Robert M. Anderson, Jr., of the Resnsselaer Polytechnic Institute in Troy, New York. Anderson calls this selective process 'personal resonance.' It is much like the vibrating tuning fork that resonates with – or set up in vibration with – another tuning fork only if the second one possesses a similar structure, shape and size. 'Due to personal resonance, relatively few of the almost infinite variety of images in the implicate holographic structure of the universe are available to an individual's personal consciousness,' he explains. 'Thus, when enlightened persons glimpsed this unitive consciousness centuries ago,' Anderson continues, 'they did not write out relativity theory because they were not studying physics in a context similar to that in which Einstein studied physics.'

Carl Jung

Carl Jung (1875-1961) was a Swiss psychiatrist who broke away from Freudian thought over the issue of the unconscious mind as a reservoir of repressed sexual trauma. He believed in astrology, spiritualism, telepathy, telekinesis, clairvoyance, and ESP. Besides most modern western European languages, he could read several ancient ones, including Sanskrit. After the war, he traveled widely, visiting Africa, America, and India.

Entrainment of Consciousness

First observed and recorded in the seventeenth century, entrainment is a phenomenon of physics that affects us all at one time or another. You may not know it by this term; in fact you might not have even known there was a name for this quality.

Entrainment is the tendency for two oscillating bodies to lock into phase to vibrate in harmony. It is also the synchronization of two or more rhythmic cycles. This principle is universal. Entrainment appears in chemistry, pharmacology, biology, medicine, psychology, sociology, astronomy and architecture, to mention just a few disciplines. Curiously, it occurs in both living and non-living entities.

The classic example involves heart muscle. Individual heart muscle pulses at a certain rate. When different heart muscles were brought into close proximity, they all pulsed together in unison. Another example is women who live under one roof or who are closely aligned emotionally. They eventually find their menstrual cycles coincide. This even occurs to unrelated females, such as those living together in a college dormitory.

Christian Huygens, a Dutch scientist, was the first to record the effect of entrainment in 1665, quite by accident. While working on the design of a pendulum clock, he placed it next to another. He swung the pendulums at different rates, but after a period of time, he found they were swinging at the same rate.

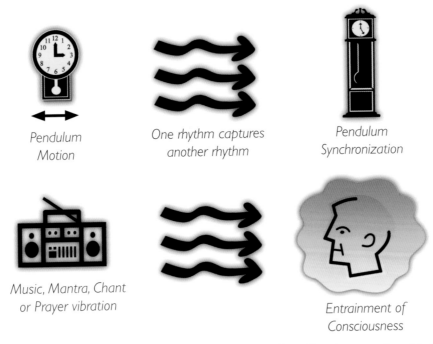

Pendulum
Motion

One rhythm captures
another rhythm

Pendulum
Synchronization

Music, Mantra, Chant
or Prayer vibration

Entrainment of
Consciousness

The entrainment phenomenon is most evident in music. In this discipline there are three kinds of entrainment: rhythmic, melodic and dynamic. Entrainment in music potentially moves the listener in three ways. It resonates with the listener's feelings; it transforms negative feelings into positive and it promotes either a state of liveliness or serenity. Certain sounds in a specific sequence, moreover, can take the listener from one place to another.

Similarly, entrainment of consciousness is the principle at work for the repetition of *mantras*, chants and the effectiveness of prayers.

States of Consciousness

Even as a falcon or an eagle, after soaring in the sky,
folds his wings for he is weary, and flies down to his nest,
even so the Spirit of man hastens to that place of rest
where the soul has no desires and the Spirit sees no dreams.

--from the Upanishads

Each one of us lives within a cycle of consciousness that revolves around three states: awake, dream and deep-sleep. During our waking state, we live and perceive the world all of us share when we are not sleeping. Our world consists of the physical objects and beings, as well as the thoughts and emotions that go with this state. The waking world, for each of us, disappears when we fall asleep at night, leaving this state of consciousness behind for several hours. We then begin to experience the cycles of the other two phases of consciousness when we sleep.

In the dream state, we again experience a world of objects and beings, emotions and thoughts that may appear vastly different at times from our waking world. The characteristics of this phase of our life belong solely to the person who is dreaming. As we leave the dream world, it, too, disappears.

The deep-sleep phase of our consciousness is unlike the other two. Here, there is no world of objects and beings, thoughts and emotions. There exists only a blankness – a nothingness. This is experienced only by the person whose consciousness has entered the deep-sleep stage and not for the dreamer or the waker. This world also disappears when we exit it.

These are all conditioned states. The Pure Consciousness, conditioned by the causal body becomes the deep-sleeper. The Consciousness conditioned by the subtle and gross bodies becomes the dreamer and waker respectively. Imagine looking at a pail of water through three different color glasses, red, yellow and black. When viewed through each separate glass, the water acquires that color. However, when the glasses are removed, the water is actually clear. Similarly, Pure Consciousness gets conditioned by the physical, subtle and causal bodies.

Our causal body is composed of *vasanas*, the seed, which blossoms into the individual personality. The causal body manifests first as the subtle body, molded by thought, emotions and desires.

In turn, the subtle body manifests as the gross body, which perceives and acts. The structure and behavior of the gross body depends on the nature of the subtle body. Similarly, the subtle body's nature depends on the quality of the causal one. If the causal form is the seed, then the subtle body is the sapling that emerges from the seed and the gross body is the tree.

We are all familiar with the dream and waking states of consciousness. The deep-sleep phase, though, may be a new idea. While we are in it, nothing else exists. Many people, including philosophers and psychologists, have ignored this portion of our sleeping hours, dismissing this time without any thorough examination of it.

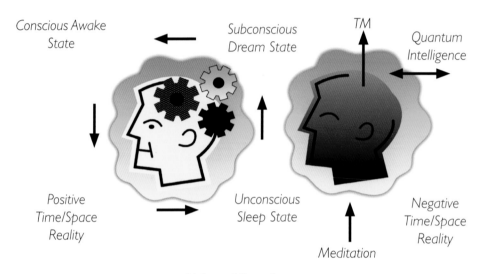

The Vedic masters know that this part of the cycle – just like the other two – is vital to who you are. What we assume is nothingness is actually our seed body, out of which emerge both the dreamer and the waker. The nothingness causes the individual to emerge out of it. A doctor goes to sleep and wakes up a doctor. Just as a philosopher goes to sleep and awakes the next morning as a philosopher or a painter emerges from sleep as a painter.

If each of us wakes up as ourselves, then there must be a continuity while we are in this part of the cycle. Our individuality exists in seed form even though we remember nothing of it. In fact, out of a multitude of seeds – all of which is a vast nothingness – spring forth a multitude of persons everyday.

Western philosophy draws its ideas mostly from the waking state, paying slight attention to the dream stage and even less notice of the deep-sleep phase.

Relying heavily on *only* the awake stage of consciousness, Western philosophers attempt to solve the mysteries of the universe. Unfortunately, the data gathered from one-third of the natural cycle of consciousness is not adequate to solve these timeless enigmas. We are destined to draw the wrong conclusions with this myopic approach.

Indian Vedic tradition, on the other hand, seriously examines all three states – the gross, subtle and causal bodies as well as the three states of consciousness. This ancient wisdom dismisses none of it in its attempt to reach absolute Reality – the state of Pure Consciousness. Consciousness in its pure state is homogenous: One and one alone.

Reality is defined as that which existed in the past, exists in the present and will still exist in the future. It has no beginning, middle or end.

Only that which exists eternally is Real. Similarly, that which is temporary, only existing for a limited time, is considered not real. If you apply this definition to the three states of consciousness, not one of them qualifies as Reality. Each one is genuine for only as long as we are residing in that phase.

So there must be something more, something that meets the definition of Reality.

The Fourth State

You know yourself only as a waker, a dreamer or a deep-sleeper. What you do not know is that Your Real Self is the Unconditioned Consciousness. It is the substratum of the three experiences, which you have been believed into yourself to be.

In all of these phases, you refer to yourself in the first person, as 'I'. But these three distinct and different phases of unequal factors can never be the 'I'.

What you refer to as 'I', is apart from them. It is really the Self that holds the three personalities together. This is the Pure Consciousness, the fourth state, known as *turiya*. In fact, *turiya* means fourth. It is the supreme state of peace and bliss. Those few throughout history who have reached this pinnacle explain that it is the absolute state of fulfillment. The ancient seers have long described this as a vast field, one that is unbounded and undivided by objects and beings, thoughts and emotions and individual experiences.

This is the same consciousness that the quantum physicists have discovered. In their investigations, they reach conclusions astonishingly similar to those the Vedic masters did thousands of years ago. These eminent scientific thinkers grasp the ultimate paradox of its nature: it is emptiness – a void. Yet, it also possesses an essential fullness.

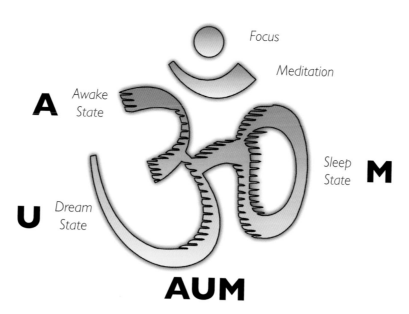

Although this state of Reality contains nothing in a concretely manifest form, It does indeed hold all of existence in potential. It is not so much a vacuum as a plenum: nothing is missing in it. The ultimate source of all existence, this Cosmic Consciousness is pregnant with the possibility of everything there is. The world around us is Its creation. It is the realization and concretization of its inherent potential.

Vedic masters and ancient seers have told us that this is our primary Self. It is our true, original nature and it is the state we try to regain. The Self Realized person merges with the infinite Consciousness as a river flows and merges into the ocean. An experience that transcends all experiences, it cannot be translated physically, emotionally or intellectually.

We can only become that eternal Being by shedding the conditioned states of the waker, dreamer and deep-sleeper. This fourth plane of Pure Consciousness is impossible to capture through the world of the waker. Nor can it be realized while we are in the dream or the deep-sleep state.

The Vedic masters assure us that the Self is not out of reach. We all can gain access to this state of absolute peace and bliss by merging with the Self. Not only are we able to gain this ultimate peace, but the Vedic tradition tells us that this is our purpose of life.

When we shift our focus from the external material world and pursue the Pure Consciousness, we inch closer to greater peace and joy. The longer we pursue this, the closer we are to reaching it, and the more bliss and peace we acquire. Though the Real Self is neither an object nor a perception, the person who seeks it soon sees Its radiance in all his experiences of his life. Each day is filled with a greater and deeper contentment. When, finally, his consciousness merges with that of the Cosmic Consciousness, he gains the absolute bliss of spiritual Enlightenment.

This ultimate state can be experienced in meditation, when we shed our waking, dream and deep sleep conditionings.

Underlying the three states of human consciousness there is a unified, nonlocalized and subtle layer: Pure Consciousness. To obtain it you must give your personality a lift to your real Being. You will then lift the entire world. When you make the move to the central core of your personality, you become the axle around which the world revolves.

Om

Omnipotent. *Omnipresent. Omniscient.*

It is no coincidence that the highest word in expressing the Supreme Absolute is 'Om.' It is the only word – in any language – that is totally without any gender connotations and void of any declension of any kind. It is impossible to alter this word. Om signifies that immutable principle which is nameless and formless, the super consciousness which never undergoes change.

Om is indefinable.

Om is indefinable to such a degree that even this statement is considered to be an attempt at defining it. The moment you define it you limit it. Once you make the statement that the word is indefinable you no longer are in the realm of Om, but are making a formal statement.

To avoid this – and not to trick ourselves into thinking that when we talk of Om we are raising our consciousness to infinity – we speak of *Brahman*.

The *Mandukya Upanishad* provides us with a detailed explanation of this transcosmic sound and its significance. The *Upanishads* record the ancient dialogues between the great masters and their closest disciples between the fifteenth and fifth centuries before Christ.

Om is the awakened life of supreme consciousness. It is the Spirit itself, that which cannot be touched nor seen, that which is above all distinction, beyond thought. It is peace and love.

Atman is the eternal Word Om. It's composed of three sounds, 'A,' 'U,' and 'M' which correspond to the three states of consciousness. The first sound 'A,' is the first state of waking consciousness, common to all people, found in the word, *apti*, attaining, and *adimatvam*, being first. Those who know this attain all their desires and in all things become first.

'U,' the second sound and the second state, that of dreaming consciousness, is the sound found in the words, *utkarsha* or uprising and *ubhayatvam*, 'bothness.' Those who know this raises the traditions of knowledge and attains equilibrium. The person who knows this sound, the *Mandukya Upanishad* says, will never have a family member who does not know *Brahman*.

'M,' the third sound of Om is the third state of sleeping consciousness. Its sound is found in the words *miti*, measure and *mi* to end. It gives *apiti* its 'final end.' Who knows this, the *Upanishad* declares, measures with his mind and attains the final End.

The word Om as one sound is the fourth state of supreme consciousness.

It is beyond the senses and is the end of evaluations. It is non-duality and love. He goes with his self to the supreme Self who knows this, who knows this.

-- *Mandukya Upanishad, 1500 B.C*

Death and Consciousness

If energy, indeed, can never be created and never be destroyed, then what happens to the subtle body at the time of death?

It is well known that the physical body is shed. Customarily, it is buried or cremated. It is at this time that the energy link of *prana* or aliveness between the subtle and the gross body is severed. This kinetic energy is then returned to the free energy of the universe.

The entire energy field of awareness shifts from the physical to the subtle and causal bodies, and comes to a quintessence. A panorama of memories flashes before a person at the moment of death, as evidenced in the description of many who say 'My whole life flashed before my eyes.' This life review – completed in an instant of earthly time – has been reported over and over in near-death experiences. Amazingly, each and every person reported 'seeing the light' and report it was a 'being' of light that was indescribably brilliant and comforting.

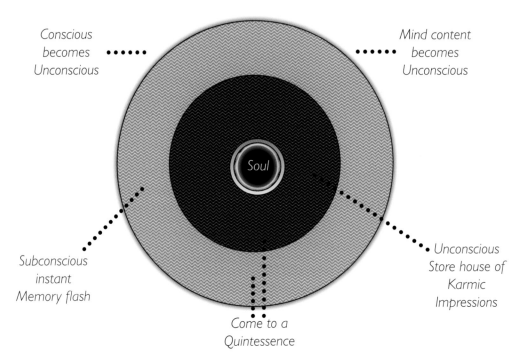

The awareness then encapsulates this light or the pure Self, transmigrating only to reincarnate. This explains the 'circle of life' and how we are ultimately influenced by our previous subliminal impressions or memories – contained in the subtle and causal bodies – which are 'carried over' from life cycle to life cycle. This awareness – or potential energy – is an ever-evolving continuum.

Between death and rebirth, it is the memory, or the karmic impressions within the subtle and causal plane that creates 'heaven' or 'hell' for the departed soul. There is no physical existence of heaven and hell as such; each is merely a state of mind. The mind content unfolds upon itself.

The experiences of an entire lifetime are contained within the subtle body. It is our durable subtle body that contains timeless, spaceless circles of indestructible energy. Through our thoughts, actions and behaviors, we can either fortify or nourish these vortices of inner intelligence, or we can starve and contaminate the information that is 'carried over.'

The total sum of all present and past experiences determines the direction of the transmigrating body. The type of compatible 'fertilized field' it enters for its next incarnation will depend on the quality of its contents.

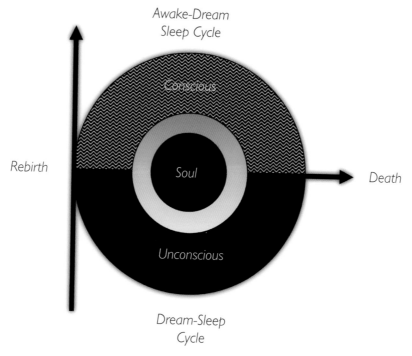

During our time between lives, we are only experiencing a truncated version of the awake, dream and sleep cycle. In this period, we only dream and sleep, since there is no physical body to be awake in. However, this is significant because it is the dream stage between lives that creates an individual's heaven or hell – it involves the unfolding of our karmic impressions.

Chakras

Most of the functions of our body go unseen. Many occur in the biocosm, in the world that is much too small to be seen with the naked eye. In a similar fashion, there exists an unseen – yet very real – connection between the seven major *chakras* and our physical and mental being.

A *chakra* is a specialized center of energy within our subtle bodies. Its name comes from the Sanskrit word for wheel. The ancient Vedic masters described these invisible energy fields as whirling vortices that consume higher energies, and then transmute these to a form the human body can use. Each *chakra* is connected to another and to its own specific specialized position of our physical-cellular structure through fine, subtle energetic channels known as *nadis*.

In effect, each *chakra* transforms a higher level of energy into a lower form and frequency the body can use. The body, in turn, translates this energy into a form that produces the necessary hormonal, physiologic and ultimately cellular changes.

Each *chakra* is a multi-dimensional center with its own particular psychic and physical function. Each one communicates with the cells through both the nervous system and the endocrine system, producing neurohormonal reactions that affect our moods and our behavior. The field of psycho-neuro-immunology echoes the existence of *chakras* as well as the deeper unseen connections among the brain, the endocrine glands and the immune system.

Dr. Hiroshi Motoyama's research is breaking new ground in this field. He recorded multiple electrical samples of *chakras* from several individuals advanced in meditation. When the individual claimed a particular *chakra* had been 'awakened,' an electrode, which had previously been placed over the designated area, recorded a greater amplitude and frequency in the electrical field. Notably, this was significantly greater than the energy recorded from the *chakras* of those in the control group. Motoyama successfully reproduced the results many times in his studies.

His findings were also duplicated by Itzhak Bentov, a Czechoslovak researcher. He used equipment similar to Motoyama's. Bentov's work helped to prove the emission of potential electrostatic energy from a *chakra*.

The presence of high frequency *chakras* oscillations were demonstrated by Dr. Valerie hunt. This UCLA professor, the first to report this in scientific literature, found that the normal frequency of brain waves lies within a range of up to 100 cycles per second. The range where the most information is generated runs up to 30 cycles per second. The frequency of muscle rises to 225 cycles per second, while that of the heart goes as high as 250 cycles per second.

*Transform
Higher
energies*

*Psychic and
physical function*

*Neurohormonal
connections*

*1600 cycles/sec
Sub harmonic
frequency*

*Carried over
impressions*

*Acquired
Impressions
repository*

Contrast this with the readings for the *chakras*. They have an accelerated frequency of between 100 to 1600 cycles per second – higher than anything that has been recorded from the human body. This high-frequency range is, in fact, a sub-harmonic of an original *chakra* signal, which is in the range of many thousands cycles per second.

Dr. Hunt also used the talents of trained psychic clairvoyant, Rosilyn Bruyere. Dr. Hunt electronically monitored the *chakras* by EMG electrodes. Simultaneously, Bruyere observed the person's subtle energy or 'auric field' – rings of color surrounding the bodies of living things. Bruyere was not allowed to see the results during the experiment so there could be no influencing the readings.

The clairvoyant's observation of the 'auric fields' correlated remarkably well with electronic readings. Each color was associated with a different EMG wave pattern. When Bruyere described a person's aura as red, for example, the monitor displayed the red wave pattern.

The *chakras* contain the 'carried over' impressions and play a detrimental role in the development of the fetus. They are also the repository for acquired impressions.

Hiroshi Motoyama

Dr. Hiroshi Motoyama, a well-known Japanese scholar, was born in Japan in 1925. He graduated from the Tokyo University of Literature and Science with Ph.D. degrees in Philosophy and Physiological Psychology, and has received several prestigious awards for his work in the comparative study of Eastern and Western mysticism. He is the author of over 50 books and was selected one of the world's leading parapsychologists by UNESCO in 1974.

Chakras and Nadis

The *chakras* are connected to each other as well as to portions of the physical cellular structure through the subtle energy channels of *nadis*. Formed by fine threads of subtle energetic matter, *nadis* are a vast network of fluid-like energies paralleling the bodily nerves. They are not to be confused with arteries, veins or nerves. Because of their intricate interconnection with the nerve plexus and their unique alignment with the endocrine glands, the *nadis* influence the nature and quality of nerve transmission.

Chakras also create changes in the cells through the hormonal link. Various sources report the ancient Vedic masters deciphered up to 72,000 – or more – *nadis* or etheric channels in the subtle anatomy of human beings.

Amazingly, this ancient description of *nadis* and *chakras* bears a remarkable resemblance to the contemporary anatomical layout of the nerves and plexuses. Yet not one Master dissected a physical body to discover this network. Even if they had, it would not have made a difference, since *nadis* and *chakras* are part of our unseen connection to the Spirit.

Instead, these wise sages discovered this subtle energy network through introspective experimentation. It is this invisible link of the *chakra* to the physical body that is the secret to our health and vitality.

Each individual *chakra* is also characterized by a specific color, a unique shape and a corresponding resonant *mantra*, the syllabic vibration used in advanced meditation.

The *chakras* in ancient Vedic tradition are visualized as beautiful lotus flowers. The roots of these flowers symbolize the fine, delicate *nadis* that provide nourishment throughout the system. The *chakras* disperse the vital life force and energy into the physical body – from the root to the limb and up into the highest branches.

Kundalini is the energy that activates the *chakras* and assists in the higher awareness. Described as a 'coiled serpent,' it lies dormant at the first major *chakra*. It is, however, poised to spring into action at any time. Unfortunately for most individuals, this energy never gets used.

The potential energy of awareness in each individual is polarized. There exists the positive polarity at the *sahasara* or crown and the negative polarity, *kundalini*, which lies dormant at the base of the spine. Despite the very real fact that we have an infinite reservoir of *kundalini* energy, we use only a small fraction of what is available to us. Moreover, the abundant, magnificent power of this energy has yet to even be imagined by 'official' science.

You have met individuals who possess an abundance of energy, insight and creativity. Dynamic geniuses and miracle performers appear in every era and in every culture. These incredible individuals who seem to be the exception rather than the rule, credit their 'otherworldly' talents and perceptions to a whole host of reasons: psycho kinesis, 'ESP', telepathy, astral travel or other supernatural or religious phenomenon.

Yet, what is not recognized is that such individuals have learned to unleash the latent power of *kundalini* energy within. These rare individuals have discovered the unseen connection: the unconscious world.

The *kundalini* power contains latent memories – both personal and transpersonal. Our way of understanding it is in terms of the unconsciousness when the power is unleashed in a coordinated fashion, as in structured meditation, this serpentine energy slowly dances up the spinal column as a wave of beauty and bliss. Along the way, it awakens the buds of the *chakras* and the lotus flowers blossom.

This blossoming is described by Sir John Woodroffe: When *Shakti*, the feminine *kundalini* power is asleep, one is awake to the external world. But when she awakens and unites with the masculine *sahasara* or *Shiva* at the crown, then one becomes asleep to the world and immersed in pure awareness.

As a potential power, *kundalini* sustains ordinary awareness, but when she unites with *sahasara*, she ascends to a state or high, that of pure awareness. Her ascent embodies the process of evolution in which we as human beings come to realize our full potential.

This energy unravels within us like a flowing river, providing us with a constant source of inner power. In Gita Mehta's *A River Sutra,* the bureaucrat who has retired by the river says that *'In the silence of the ebbing night, I sometimes think I can hear the river's heartbeat pulsing under the ground before she reveals herself at last to the anchorites of Shiva deep in meditation...'*

It is said the divine *Shiva,* or the *Creator and Destroyer of Worlds,* blessed the river and named it *Narmada,* or *Delightful One.* With her eternal and inexhaustible energy, the river symbolizes the dance between the human and the divine, much like the *kundalini* unwinds the energy that is both personal and universal.

As the undulating energy enters its final abode -- near the 'third eye' and crown -- a sensation of light floods the meditative being, or microcosm. It is a beautiful union, quite like the marriage between the masculine *sahasara* energy and the feminine *kundalini* energy. There is then an infinite expansion of awareness... and the dance begins.

Centers of Consciousness

The *chakras* vitally regulate the various states of awareness. Situated in the subtle body, the seven *chakras* are in the 'same latitude' as specific parts of the physical body. They ascend from the base of the spine to the crown of the head.

Vedas associate what has occurred in a person's present and past lifetimes with the function or dysfunction of *chakras.* Wellness or illness first starts in this energy dimension, and is later manifested in the physical body. This hidden physiology is the force behind the physical body.

If our energy field is distorted--if these vortices are gradually diminished and broken altogether--physical disease soon follows. This explains why some people seem immune to ill health while others are subject to disease.

Located at the base of the spine, the root *chakra* reflects our connectedness to the Earth, or how grounded we are. The root is the seat of the *kundalini,* and pertains to our physical existence. Psychologically, it is linked to our basic, primitive survival instincts, such as fear of injury or bodily harm. When integrated, it can provide us with a sense of stability and security. When we feel threatened, our root *chakra* activates the 'flight or fight response' mechanism, so we are better prepared for crisis or danger.

Over activity, however, may manifest negatively as insecurity, irrational or phobic fear, paranoia and anxiety. Too much energy invested here may make a person fearful, over-anxious and defensive. It is here that accumulated stress is released and the associated physical organs of excretion – the rectum, anal canal and urethra – symbolize this process.

The sacral *chakra* is closely related to the root *chakra.* They both refer to the processes of digestion and elimination. Dysfunction in these lower two *chakras* may indicate an inability to release or let go. Corresponding physical ailments of constipation, irritable bowel syndrome, and colon cancer, may manifest as a result.

The root *chakra* is also linked with the reproductive functions of the sperm and ovum. The cosmic, creative *kundalini* potential emanating from the root *chakra* is both procreative and artistic in nature. The energy used to create new life is the same as for creating poetry, art and music. Both infertility and lack of expression may be associated with this *chakra* dysfunction.

The sacral *chakra* is the subtle seat of sexuality symbolized in the release of bodily fluids at the level of sexual organs. It is associated with the testes and ovaries, and hormone production.

The sacral *chakra* involves complex sensual emotions of love and attentiveness, as well as sexual expression. An over emphasis on sexuality spares little energy for higher pursuits or other types of creativity. Individuals whose energies are centered primarily in this *chakra* will tend to only seek out sexual relationships, and view others as nothing more than sexual objects. Ailments and illnesses resulting from such dysfunction may include gynecological problems in women, bladder tumors, lower back pain, colitis, prostatitis, cancer of the cervix and other reproductive organs, and sexually transmitted disease.

The navel or solar plexus *chakra* supplies nutritive subtle energy to most of the major digestive organs, including the stomach, the large intestine, pancreas, liver, gall bladder, and adrenal glands. The food burns in the digestive system, and the process releases active energy throughout the body. Unregulated and improper digestion is destructive, in that it contributes to upset stomach, heartburn and ulcers.

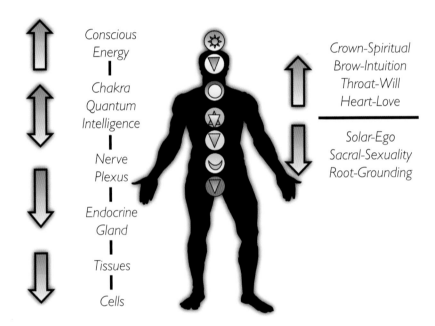

The navel *chakra* influences the amount of control we have over our lives, and can be a source of dynamic energy. Because it is linked to personal power, it can either be a source of confidence and contentment, or disillusionment, discontent and jealousy. The source of all anger is frustrated desire or feeling powerless. Abnormal functioning of this *chakra* not only manifests in a short temper and abusive behavior, but also creates inner conflict. Some psychological studies of ulcer patients, in fact, reveal that they often take on too many dominant responsibilities while viewing themselves as incapable. In this way, they alternate between dominance and submission.

The solar plexus *chakra* is also closely related to the adrenal glands, which play an important role in times of stress. Weakness, easy fatigue and vulnerability to infection and disease set in when there is blockage in this *chakra*. The inner need for control may stem from an imbalance in the *chakra*, and on a physical level, those with diabetes experience a loss of personal power when they become insulin dependent.

This transitional *chakra* mediates between the three lower, earthly energies and the three higher, spiritual energies. At the heart *chakra* – the center of equilibrium – these two 'worlds' meet and converge. As the element of air, the fourth *chakra* is said to occupy the space between heaven and Earth. Most negative emotions arise out of the root, sacral and solar plexus *chakras*, since they are more primitive in nature. These centers below the diaphragm are primarily concerned with physical desires. By integrating our awareness at this *chakra*, we become more enlightened.

The heart *chakra* is our emotional center, relating to our interactions with other people. A wave of energy sweeps over the heart when we experience strong, positive feelings toward another person. This sensation may manifest in feeling 'swept off our feet' when we fall in love. An open-heart *chakra* is integral to our ability to express compassion, unconditional love and altruism.

Epitomized by the bond between mother and child, it is no coincidence that the breasts are located at the level of this *chakra* and are the only organs dedicated to the nurturing of another being. Developing compassion and empathy for others is a consequence of loving, and being loved in turn. We cultivate the sense that the world does not revolve around us completely, and that there are others to consider.

Blockages in the heart *chakra* may derive from an inability to love or regard others, and also arises from lack of self-love. They can suppress the immune systems, and immuno-suppression leads to malignancies. Autoimmune diseases like rheumatoid arthritis, primary ovarian failure, adrenal atrophy and diabetes, and even coronary artery disease may also be indirectly attributed to *chakra* dysfunction. Psycho-neuro-immunology researchers have found that patients suffering from severe depression, loneliness and grief suffered low activity of the thymus gland, and decreased T-lymphocytes – or T-cells that fight infections – count.

Often, a blockage in one *chakra* affects another. For example, frequent sexual contacts may be the result of a sacral *chakra* blockage and may promote positive HIV status. Because of poor self-image associated with negative cultural views, an imbalance occurs in the heart *chakra* as well. This leads to thymic dysfunction and immuno-suppression, causing full expression of the disease. Modern science fails to recognize the importance of such *emotional immunity*, when it comes to the expression from 'carrier state' to full-blown illness.

Symbolic of its position around the vocal cords, the throat *chakra* is essentially a communicative and a center for creativity. The energies of many artists are concentrated here. This *chakra* is also the center of will and encourages us to communicate with one another as well as to verbally express new ideas.

It transfers energy to the thyroid, parathyroid gland and the larynx. Inadequate energy flow to the flow to the throat *chakra* is most notable in over or under activity in the thyroid gland, laryngitis and cancer of the lungs, larynx, throat and mouth. Lack of expression literally silences us, so that our negative emotions become bottled up inside. If they are never vented, or given a means of expression, they eventually manifest physically, and cause damage.

The 'third eye,' or the brow *chakra*, is represented by the energy polarity between the pituitary gland and the pineal glands. This third eye is the seat of intuition and clairvoyance. Practicing meditation develops your intuition as well as sharpening the activity of the third eye *chakra*. Inward focusing, or introspection, results in clear insight and the power of discernment. Because the center rests between the eyebrows, this *chakra* is the source of our intellect and wisdom. Our ears, eyes, nose and sinuses reside at this level, as do the origin of the spinal cord pineal and pituitary gland.

Chakra dysfunction at this level can result in major endocrine imbalances. Recent scientific research in the field of physcho-neuro-immunology has also revealed the deeper connections among the mind, the endocrine and the immune systems.

The seventh *chakra* bears the name *sahasara*, or 'thousand rayed.' The final *chakra* has no corresponding element, color or sound because the Absolute Self that governs it is beyond all quality. Situated at the crown of the head, it is a lotus flower with a thousand petals radiating splendor.

Inner World

Namaste … I honor the place in you in which the entire universe dwells. I honor the place in you, which is of love, of peace, of light and of truth. When you are in that place in you, and I am in that place in me … We are One.

--Inspired by Yoga literature

How does our physical self responds to transitions in our awareness? How do we explain this inner experience?

The brain is the 'central processing unit' of our body and acts much like a computer. With its extension, the spinal cord, it makes up the central nervous system. Neuro-chemicals form the link between the brain – our *hardware* – and the mind – our *software*. The electrical circuits, or nerves, in the body belong to two powerful systems that transmit information for processing and carry out messages from the brain.

The first is the voluntary or sensorimotor nervous system, which controls both our senses and the muscles, providing the body with information about the inner sensations as well as the outer environment. The other system is called the involuntary or autonomic nervous system. This regulates our internal organ systems, such as circulation and digestion.

The autonomic nervous system is a sophisticated network of unseen energy that maintains the balance and harmony in the body. It is called 'autonomic' because it functions largely outside the bounds of conscious control. It is primarily involved with controlling our stress reactions. If we know how to 'tame' this powerful system, we can free ourselves from stress and the diseases associated with it.

The limbic system, often called the 'seat of human emotion' and the hypothalamus, influence our 'inner world.' The hypothalamus is a small, powerful brain 'microchip,' to continue the computer analogy that sits at the base of the brain. It receives messages from 'higher' brain centers, and governs both the endocrine and the autonomic nervous system. It is known as the 'brain's brain' and the mind's 'gateway to health.' It also corresponds to the brow *chakra* – the central focus of meditation.

The two limbs of the autonomic system – sympathetic and parasympathetic – work to keep the bodily organs under a dual control. They, however, are not polar opposites, but rather are complimentary systems. Like our right and left-hand work together, a dynamic equilibrium exists between the two limbs when we are healthy. Both systems innervate the heart, for example.

Under normal circumstances, a balance between the two limbs determines the resting heart rate – about 70 beats per minute. Sympathetic stimulation speeds up the heart rate and creates arousal in the body. The parasympathetic, on the other hand, slows the heart rate and induces inhibition or rest in the body.

If we feel threatened, our sympathetic system provides the alarm or arousal for defense – the familiar 'flight or fight response.' Those tense muscles you feel every day is due to this system. When we are startled, feel under attack, or encounter daily stress, our whole body reacts, resulting in muscle tension.

By contrast, the parasympathetic system for the most part generates an inhibitory response. It is site-specific. It is in fact the system responsible, for example, for slowing the beating of the heart. It is this part of the body's processing center that is responsible a fainting spell from fear of pain or from actual pain even in the face of overall arousal. We never use only one half of our autonomic nervous system.

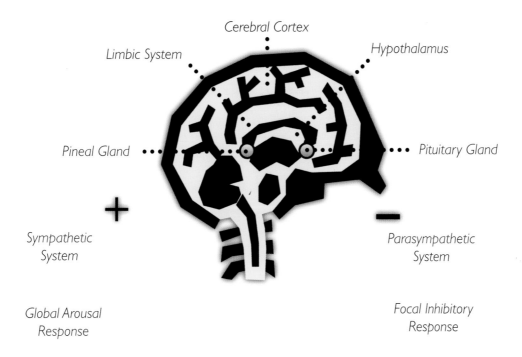

Cerebral Cortex

Limbic System

Hypothalamus

Pineal Gland

Pituitary Gland

+

−

Sympathetic
System

Parasympathetic
System

Global Arousal
Response

Focal Inhibitory
Response

Both limbs are stimulated by environmental stress, however. It is our individual reaction to the perceived threat that determines the neurological balance. The two systems are not only built differently, but also function differently. The sympathetic coordinates an overall 'global' response, while the parasympathetic is 'focal' or specific. That means we have almost infinite permutations and combinations between arousal and inhibition.

Stress is a state of autonomic imbalance characterized by an excessive dominance of either arousal or inhibition or a complex interaction of the two. Acute stress is most often thought of as just a 'flight or fight response,' culminating in a rise in blood pressure, heart rate, breathing and an increase in muscle tension. Our thoughts and perceptions determine the intensity of the alarm reaction.

Even when the threat disappears, it leaves a subtle, residual alertness in our subconscious. For instance, a workaholic – because of the urgency of time – has that residual impression. This is the source of chronic stress, which prevents us from completely relaxing. When we think there is danger – even if there really is none – we react like there is. In this way, small day-to-day worries build into larger more formidable issues.

If this continues, or if new threats should arise, our body depletes its resources and we feel the result in that 'burned out' feeling of being easily fatigued and experiencing general exhaustion. Remaining in a state of constant arousal – without seek relief – sets the stage for physiological breakdown in the form of illness, disease and even premature death.

Meditation can correct this imbalance of the two energy systems, infusing the body and mind with strength to withstand the stress in the environment.

Thoughts, therefore, are very powerful influences over our physical – as well as our mental – well being. While we mistakenly believe thoughts to be ephemeral entities, in and of themselves harmless, they indeed are much more powerful.

Perception

Human Perception

It isn't that the world of appearances is wrong: it isn't that there aren't objects out there, at one level of reality. It's that if you penetrate through and look at the universe with a holographic system, you arrive at a different view, a different reality. And that other reality can explain things that have hitherto remained inexplicable scientifically: paranormal phenomena, synchronicities, the apparently meaningful coincidence of events.

--Karl Pribram in an interview in Psychology Today

Where does the brain store memories?
How does the brain store them?

These were the questions that puzzled Pribram and eventually led him toward the holographic model of perception. When he first began his investigations, in the 1940s, the accepted scientific theory viewed memories as being localized in the brain itself. Each memory, it was thought, had a specific location in specific brain cells.

These memory traces were dubbed engrams. No one knew what exactly the engrams were. Some thought they were neurons; others believed they were a specialized molecule. Whatever their composition, though, most scientists were confident it was only a matter of time before they would be found.

There were reasons for this confidence in the scientific community. Wilder Penfield, a Canadian neurosurgeon, offered convincing evidence in the 1920s that individual memories resided in their own locations within the brain itself.

Penfield discovered this quite by accident while operating on the brains of epileptics. It is an unusual feature of the brain that the object itself does not sense pain directly. If the scalp and skull are deadened with a local anesthetic, surgery can be performed on the brain of a fully conscious person without inflicting any pain.

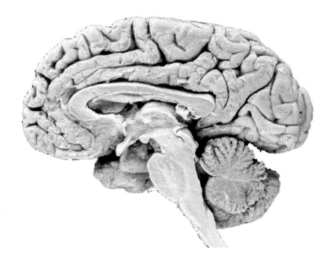

Penfield discovered that while he operated on fully conscious epileptics, he could electrically stimulate various areas of their brain cells. He further found, much to his amazement that when he stimulated the temporal lobes – the area of the brain behind the temples – the patient relived memories of past events.

One man relived a conversation he had with friends in South Africa. A boy not only heard his mother talking on the telephone, but after several touches from Penfield's electrodes, was able to repeat it word for word. A woman found herself in her kitchen and could hear her son playing outside.

Even when Penfield attempted to mislead his patients by telling them he was stimulating a different area when in reality he wasn't, the patient's stimulus evoked the exact same memory.

It was obvious to Penfield that everything we have ever experienced is recorded in our brain, from the urgent to the insignificant. Every stranger's face we have ever glanced at in a crowd is resides someplace in the brain. He reasoned that this is why so many memories of so many unimportant events continues to surface. If our memory is a complete and unabridged record of even the most mundane of our daily experiences, then it is reasonable to assume that dipping randomly into such a massive chronicle would produce a good deal of trifling information. It was only a matter of time, the scientific community – and Pribram included – that the engram would be identified and classified.

But in the 1940s, startling research would destroy that theory. Pribram worked with Karl Lashley at the Yerkes Laboratory of Primate Biology, then located in Orange Park, Florida. Lashley searched for the elusive engram. Lashley though not only failed to discover it, but his research appeared to indicate it never existed.

Lashley trained rats to run through a maze. Then he surgically removed various parts of their brains and retested the animals. He sought to literally cut out the portions of the brain where the memory of running the maze resided. But no matter the area of the physical brain he took out, he could not remove the memory of running the maze. The rats' motor skills might be impaired because of the extraction of specific portions of the brain, but their memories remained stubbornly intact.

Pribram reasoned that if memories were not located at specific sites within the physical brain, they were instead distributed throughout the organ as a whole. It was not until the 1960s that the first hologram was constructed. And it provided him a solution to the decades-long puzzle.

If it was possible for every piece of the holographic film to contain all the information necessary to create a whole image, then it seemed equally plausible that every segment of the brain contained all of the information necessary to recall an entire memory.

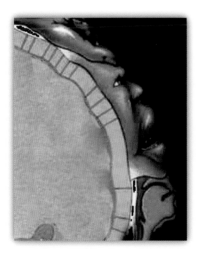

Wilder Graves Penfield

Wilder Graves Penfield (1891-1976) was born in the United States, completed his undergraduate education there and in England, served during World War I in France, qualified as a medical doctor and practiced in the United States and did not migrate to Canada until he was 37 years old. He developed a map of the brain, often portrayed as a cartoon called the motor homunculus (miniature human being). During his life he was called 'the greatest living Canadian.'

Holographic Perception

I think in the twenty-first century we're going to be able to do an awful lot that we weren't able to do up to now, simply because science will be admitted to the spiritual aspects of mankind, and vice versa -- what has been segregated for at least three hundred years, since Galileo, where the spiritual aspects, in Western culture at least, have been sort of relegated over here.

-- *Karl Pribram*, Conversations On The Leading Edge Of Knowledge and Discovery

'**E**ach piece contains the whole.'

If you were to pluck a random piece out of a holographic image, you would discover that every piece contains the entire image in miniature, as we discovered earlier, with our example of the holographic apple.

So it is with our perception. At least two of the world's leading scientific minds – David Bohm, a physicist at the University of London and a former protégé of Einstein, as well as Karl Pribram, a neurophysiologist with Stanford and an architect of our contemporary understanding of the brain – believe this.

Pribram sees holography and laser physics as providing new ways of understanding how the brain stores information. An essential element in this new theory is the realization that consciousness actively participates in the process on both an individual level and a planetary scale.

Pribram thinks that when people view an object, we don't actually 'see' the image in the back of our heads or the back of our retinas. Rather we see an image in three dimensions and in the world itself. He theorizes that our viewing of an object in space, is the same location as the actual object. The object and our perception of it, therefore, coincide.

This is not too difficult to imagine if you think of your brain as a piano. When we view an object in the world, portions of the brain resonate at specific frequencies. At any given point of our attention, the brain presses selected 'notes,' which trigger strings of a certain length and a corresponding frequency. This information is then collected by the electrochemical circuits of the brain, just as the vibrations of the strings resonate throughout the piano.

In this sense – utilizing the simple act of observations – we transform the timeless, spaceless world of interference patterns into the concrete and discrete world of space and time – the world of the very apple we see.

We create both space and time on the surface of our retinas, Pribram explains. As with a hologram, the lens of the eye collects the interference patterns and converts them into three-dimensional images. This type of virtual projection is necessary for us to be able to reach out and touch an apple where it actually is and not inside our head. If we are constantly projecting images into space, then our image of the world is actually a virtual creation.

When we first notice an object, according to Pribram theory, certain frequencies resonate in the neurons in our brain. These neurons send the information regarding the frequencies to a second set of neurons. This set makes a Fourier translation, which then sends the information to another set of neurons. These construct a pattern that eventually compose the virtual image you create in space. This three-step process makes it easier for the brain to correlate the separate images.

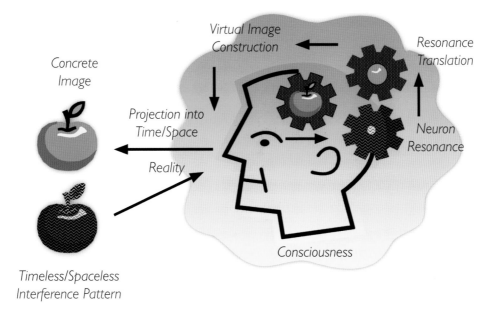

Concrete
Image

Virtual Image
Construction

Resonance
Translation

Projection into
Time/Space

Neuron
Resonance

Reality

Consciousness

Timeless/Spaceless
Interference Pattern

After the object is actually viewed, Pribram continues, the brain then processes this information in the shorthand of wave-frequency patterns. These are then scattered throughout the brain in a distributed network.

Storing memory in wave interference patterns, as in the holographic model is not only remarkably efficient, but also provides an explanation for the immense capacity of human memory.

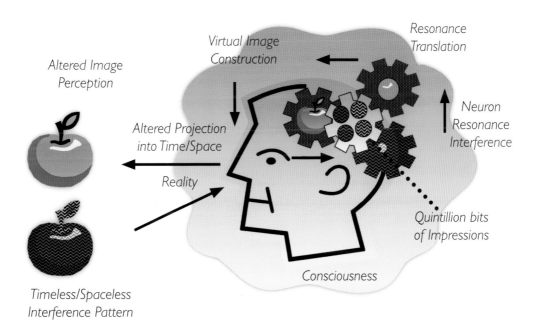

Altered Image
Perception

Virtual Image
Construction

Resonance
Translation

Altered Projection
into Time/Space

Neuron
Resonance
Interference

Reality

Quintillion bits
of Impressions

Consciousness

Timeless/Spaceless
Interference Pattern

Waves are capable of containing an unimaginable amount of data, far more than the 280 quintillion – 280,000,000,000,000,000,000 – bits of information. These supposedly constitute the average human memory, which accumulates throughout an average life span. Each of us possesses impressions that are carried over from previous lifetimes as well. These bits of memory impressions or *vasanas* – unique to the individual observer -- interfere and thus alter perception.

To illustrate the magnitude of the storage capability of holographic wave-interference patterns, the entire U.S. Library of Congress – which contains every book ever published in the English language – would fit onto a large sugar cube. This holographic model also helps to explain the instant recall of memory, often as a three-dimensional image.

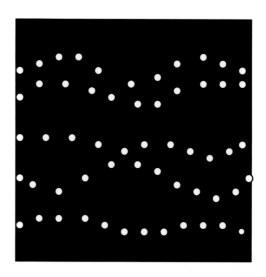

Fourier Transforms

An eighteenth-century Frenchman named Jean B.J. Fourier developed a mathematical system convert any pattern, no matter how complex, into a language of simple waves. He also showed how these waveforms could be converted back into the original pattern. The equations he developed to convert images into waveforms and back again are known as Fourier transforms.

But perhaps the most startling finding Pribram uncovered was Russian scientist Nikolai Bernstein's breakthrough that even our physical movements may be encoded in our brains as a language of Fourier waveforms. Bernstein painted white dots on dancers and filmed them against a black background. When he converted their movements into waveforms, he discovered they could be analyzed using Fourier transforms, the same mathematics Gabor used to invent the hologram.

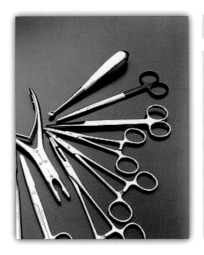

Karl Pribram

Karl Pribram, MD, Ph.D. was born February 25, 1919 in Vienna, Austria and was trained as a neurosurgeon. A long time Professor at Stanford University, he did pioneering work on the elucidation of the cerebral cortex. He is less known for his quantum approach to neurophilosophy. Author of several books and recipient of numerous awards, he is now a research professor in Psychology and Cognitive Science at Georgetown University.

Quantum Consciousness

How could wave-front decoding and transformation possibly take place?

It occurred to Pribram that wave-interference patterns might not be created in the cells themselves, but in the spaces between them. At the end of each neuron, the basic unit of a brain cell, are synapses. Here chemical charges build up, eventually triggering electrical firing across these spaces to the other neurons. In the same spaces, dendrites, the tiny filaments of nerve endings that waft back and forth, like shafts of seaweeds, communicate with other neurons. They send out and receive their own electrical wave impulses.

This is the busy hub, a place of ceaseless networking between the synapses and dendrites, where it is most likely that wave-interference patterns are assembled, analyzed and holographic images are formed.

Pribram speculated that these wave collisions created the pictorial images in our brains, similar to piano strings, which vibrate as a particular note is played. He left this to others, however, to scrutinize and test his theory, so he would not jeopardize his traditional laboratory research. For some years, the theory languished. It would take several decades for other pioneers to catch up with him.

Stuart Hameroff, an anesthesiologist from the University of Arizona, had been thinking about how anesthetic gases turn off consciousness. He suggested that it interfered with the electrical activity within the microtubules. If this, indeed, were the case, then the reverse would also be true. Electrical activity of the microtubules must somehow be at the heart of consciousness.

A group of scientists, including Pribram, Yasue, Hameroff and Scott Hagan, of the Department of Physics of McGill University each seemed to hold a piece of this puzzle. They decided to come together and collaborate. The result was a collective theory on the nature of human consciousness. According to their theory, microtubules and the membranes of dendrites were much like the 'Internet' of the human body. Every neuron of the brain would then be able to log on simultaneously and speak to every other one through the quantum processes.

Microtubules help convert and transmit discordant energy and create global coherence of the waves in the body, a process called 'superradiance.' Once coherence is achieved, the photons travel along the light pipes as if they were transparent. This phenomenon is called 'self-induced transparency.'

Photons are able to penetrate the core of the microtuble and communicate with other photons throughout the body, creating collective cooperation of subatomic particles in microtubules throughout the brain. If this were the case, it would account for the unity of thought and consciousness – the fact that we do not conceive of many disparate ideas at one time.

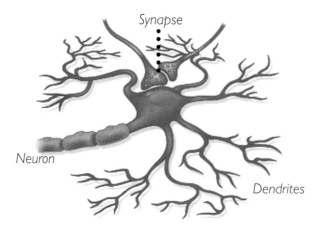

This theory also provides an explanation for the instantaneous operation of our brains, which occurs at between one ten-thousandth and one-thousandth of a second, requiring the information be transmitted at 100 to 1,000 meters per second, a speed that is greater than the capabilities of any known connections between axon or dendrites in neurons. 'Superradiance' along the light pipes would also account for the phenomenon that has been observed regularly, the tendency of EEG patterns in the brain to be synchronized.

Hameroff additionally observed that electrons glide easily along these pipes and do not get entangled in their environment. This means that they remain in a quantum state – a condition of all possible states – which enables the brain to choose from among them. This could very possibly be a good explanation for free will. At every moment, our brains are making quantum choices, taking potential states and transforming them into actual ones.

This was only a theory and had not undergone exhaustive testing, but some good mathematics and circumstantial evidence gave it weight. Fritz-Albert Popp and his biophoton emissions, along with Italian physicists Del Giudice and Preparata, had also developed experimental evidence of Hameroff's theory. All this led to the unmistakable thought that consciousness was a global phenomenon occurring everywhere in the body, not simply in our brains. Consciousness, at its most basic, was coherent light.

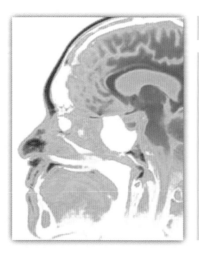

Stuart Hameroff

Stuart Hameroff, MD is Professor Emeritus at the Departments of Anesthesiology and Psychology, and Director of the Center for Consciousness Studies, at the University of Arizona. He is well known for his research on 'quantum consciousness', an alternative model to the accepted view of how consciousness arises. With Sir Roger Penrose, Dr Hameroff has proposed that consciousness arises at the quantum level within structures inside neurons, known as microtubules.

Mind-Thought-Consciousness

There is something beyond our mind, which abides in silence within our mind. It is the supreme mystery beyond thought. Let one's mind rest upon that.

-- Maitri Upanishad

Mind is a content of consciousness. It is nothing more than a flow of thoughts. When there is no thought, there is no mind. If a thought ceases to exist, then there appears a gap between that and the next thought, the substratum, which we call Consciousness, emerges.

Thoughts flow through the mind like water flows through a river. Inevitable, unending streams of thought rush past us every minute of every day. If the mind were to stop and not think for a moment and actually create a gap between two thoughts, the result would be a visible 'riverbed' beneath those thoughts. The substratum upon which those thoughts flow is our consciousness.

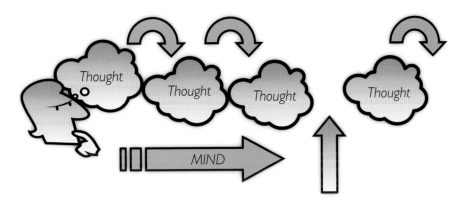

Consciousness

The only time the human mind actually stops thinking is when it is in the cycle of deep sleep. Waking or dreaming, each of us carries a never ending stream of thoughts – some positive, others negative. But all of them prevent us from really getting to know our True Reality.

Meditation is the only voluntary way to suspend thinking. Through the practice of meditation, each of us is capable of clearing our minds of thoughts and reconnecting with our consciousness.

If there is no breath, there is no thought. It is no surprise then that breath is the physical counterpart of the mind. As it conjures up images in the mind, it is essentially the mind in action. The sight of an accident, the sound of thunder, the scent of a lover's perfume … all of these things create internal dialogues to our mind and direct the way in which we breath. In each of the above situations our breathing becomes rapid and irregular.

For most of us, breath is spontaneous and is taken for granted. Like our heart beat, our breathing is involuntary. Even if we 'forget' to breath, our body switches on 'auto-pilot' and continues to breathe for us. We usually do not become aware of our breathing unless we develop conditions that limit it, like asthma or emphysema. But this powerful tool – however neglected it might be – amazingly allows us to achieve self control.

Consciousness

Breath distributes the *prana*, or aliveness, therefore providing the vital link between the mind and body. The breath affects the flow of *prana* – the fluid-like energies – in the extensive network of *nadis*. Delivering *prana* force, it provides access to the internal organs.

Prana is perceived as an air element and creates movement, pulsation, vibration and aliveness. *Prana*, we have learned, is the interface between the subtle and gross bodies. Located in the subtle body – at the confluence of *nadis* – are those seven *chakras*, or centers of awareness. The *charkas* act as transformers, directing the energy flow from the *nadis* to the major organ systems. By controlling the flow of *prana* – and *prana's* relationship to the *chakras* – the breath influences our awareness. *Prana* is not the breath itself, however, for it is the vital energy that sustains all living things by water, food, air and sunlight.

The ideal breathing motion is a smooth and unbroken wave, where the breath is even and uninterrupted. It is recorded as a perfect sine wave. By contrast, uneven breath creates turbulent thought waves and distracts us from discovering True Reality.

Think of breath as the wind, thoughts as the clouds, soul as the Sun, and consciousness as the light. A gap needs to be created in the clouds to allow for the light of consciousness to shine. This is called Enlightenment.

Thought Genesis

Pull up a chair. Let's talk.

That's your mind requesting your attention. Imagine sitting on a chair inside of your mind. Now, envision having a continuing conversation with your mind. That is a thought. Every thought you create, in reality, is in answer to the previous thought you just had. Your thoughts are a never-ending question and answer session. Thoughts are the dialogues you conduct with your mind daily.

Thoughts are energy forms and arise from the subliminal impressions or *vasanas*, stored in the deep unconscious. These are deeply embedded memories in the subtle body and are carried forth through countless life cycles during reincarnation. We are influenced by these impressions or data banks formatted by our previous and present life experiences and belief systems. Whatever we believe is what we ultimately manifest and experience.

Originating in the deep seated impressions or *vasanas*, this inner dialogue surfaces through the medium of your breath. It is the quality and quantity of your breathing, which in large degree, indicates the quality and quantity of your thoughts. Those people in meditation who have learned to slow their breath are experiencing a more relaxed, less tense dialogue of thoughts. Those whose breath are shallow and rapid are conducting an inner conversation which is tense and excitable.

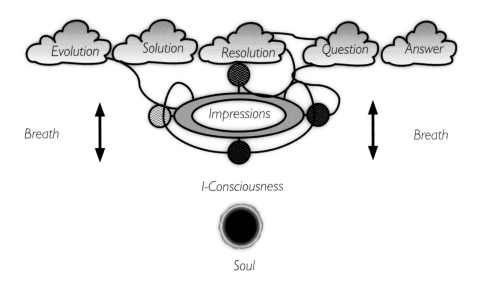

A thought originates or evolves to seek a solution to some problem or question. That thought will persist in your mind – even though it may not be in the forefront and submerged back down to the unconscious – until it finds a satisfactory resolution. The discovery of that resolution may occur in the middle of a dialogue of thoughts on another topic in a place that is least expected. That explains, why after literally hours of concentration on a specific problem, many of us find we turn to another matter, only to have the former topic resolved.

Once, however, the thought has resolved the problem or the question, the resolution is stored as a memory and will only reappear if the memory is stimulated.

Thoughts flow through the mind like water flows through a river. For many of us, our thoughts flow as if they are part of a series of rapids in a river engorged with flooding: totally out of control and with a force so ferocious we actually fear them. If the mind were to stop and not think for a moment and actually create a gap between two thoughts, the result would be a visible 'riverbed' beneath those thoughts. The substratum upon which those thoughts flow is our Pure Consciousness.

Learn to control your breathing and you begin to master your thoughts.

Speed of Thought

Imagine the Sun.

A simple request. In the time it took you to read that sentence, were you able to conceive of some image of the Sun? Perhaps you were able to visualize a large glowing disk shining in the sky.

How long did it take you to conjure up that image? A second? The request may have taken you by surprise, in which case you might have needed a few more seconds.

Surely, though, it didn't take you eight minutes, did it? Eight minutes or 480 seconds is the time it takes for the actual light from the Sun to reach the Earth at the speed of 186,000 miles per second.

So? you ask. Your thought just traveled faster than the speed of light. That makes it a *supraluminal* or a *nonlocal* event.

Scientists are finally realizing what the ancient Vedic masters knew for centuries: thoughts influence the world around us. Thoughts, unlike physical objects, can indeed move faster than the speed of light. From quantum physics to molecular biology, the mere observing of events by humans can alter the outcome to an event.

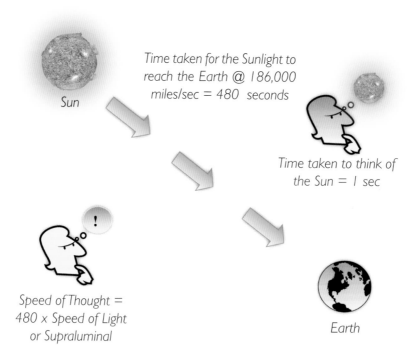

Sun

Time taken for the Sunlight to reach the Earth @ 186,000 miles/sec = 480 seconds

Time taken to think of the Sun = 1 sec

Speed of Thought = 480 x Speed of Light or Supraluminal

Earth

Thoughts that are sent into the world with intention of changing it are even more powerful, as witnessed by the experiments produced by Dr. Masaru Emoto, who amply demonstrated the vast potency of both the written and spoken words on something as basic as water.

Recall his experiments with the crystals of ice on water samples. Those crystals, which were exposed to loving and kind thoughts grew beautiful. Those crystals, however, which were linked with hostile, even hateful ideas, froze to create strange and incomplete crystals.

$$E=mc^2$$

Spirit drives this biobodysuit vehicle! After all, 99.999% of all physical 'matter' consists of vacuum, with BIG spaces between electrons and nucleus. The energy potential, or latent energy, stored in one single Hydrogen atom is equivalent to one trillion times all the energy in our universe! If our consciousness could interact with the vacuum, we could have some very BIG effects. We'll be able to use the physics of the vacuum to get to the stars.

-- William Tiller, International Congress on Science and Consciousness

Consciousness is energy. Mind is matter, the unconscious principle. It is impossible to have a thought if you are unconscious. It is not mind over matter; *it is matter over matter.*

The classical interpretation of Einstein's equation is that the energy contained within a particle equals the matter multiplied by the speed of light – 186,000 miles per second – squared. Stored within a tiny particle of matter is an unbelievable amount of potential energy.

Applying this equation to consciousness we find that consciousness, E, is equal to Mind, m, multiplied by the speed of light squared. Consciousness therefore is *supraluminal* energy. It is faster than the speed of light.

Consciousness
$$E=mc^2$$
Mind   *Speed of Light*

A more complex understanding of the equation, however, has evolved over time. This may help scientists in understanding the multidimensional nature of the universe. Einstein's equation implies matter and energy are interconvertable and interconnected.

If a particle accelerates at ever-faster speeds until it approaches the speed of light, its kinetic energy increases exponentially. At one time, most physicists accepted the apparent limitation that matter cannot accelerate beyond the speed of light.

Thought Synchronicity

The two complimentary aspects of consciousness are expressed through the right and left cerebral hemispheres. In a right-handed person, the left brain is the seat of logical thinking, representing our more analytical, mathematical, linear, verbal selves, and the right brain in turn constitutes the emotional half of the cerebral cortex, expressing our artistic, esthetic, intuitive and spatial qualities. In a left-handed person, it is just the opposite.

Thoughts, even in the subtlest dimensions, manipulate electromagnetic fields and affect one's perception. As energy waves, they vibrate. The frequency of reverberation and the distance in polarity create stress and tension; the more accelerated the frequency and wider the distance in polarity, the greater the stress.

If we think dual or discriminatory thoughts, our actions in life will usually parallel the contents of our minds. But if we think non-dual or unified and elevated thoughts, we contribute positively to human evolution.

Dual thoughts are limiting. They dwell on the 'pair of opposites'. Inherently contained in dual thoughts is wider polarity, accelerated frequency of vibration, and therefore a greater tension and stress. This leads to limited and contracted awareness: it is no wonder why an average person is essentially 85% dead to life!

Meditative thinking is more non-dual in nature. Non-dual thought has slow reverberation due to minimal distance in its polarity, and contains minimal stress. As the thought forms of meditators evolve from the dual to the non-dual, there is progression from incoherence to coherence and hence expanded awareness.

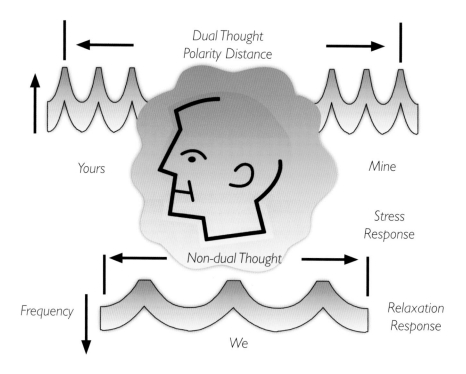

Meditators develop a sense of one equality consciousness, in which every living thing on the planet shares. They become conscious that the Self and the universe both stem from a single source. Superficial differences among people, like racial and ethnic background or religious preference, become irrelevant non-issues. When our thoughts are less fragmented, our thinking mind is free to utilize its higher functioning powers.

Such synchronization becomes evident when our brain waves are recorded as deep and slow, as *delta* waves. This leads us to a better understanding of the four brain waves: *beta, alpha, theta* and *delta*. As we progress from *beta* to *delta*, the frequency decreases, but the amplitude increases, and these frequencies correspond with the hemispheric activity in the brain. The brain is most imbalanced when the high frequency *beta* waves are predominant. (16 cycles per second). As the brain waves slow down, hemispheric synchrony dawns in the *alpha*, (10 cycles per second) and deepens in the *theta* (8 cycles per second). Total synchronization is augmented in the dominant *delta* frequency, (4 cycles per second) as it occurs exclusively during deep sleep and meditation.

During deep sleep and meditation, there is such synchronicity that it brings forth secretions of natural opiates--or what we call the endorphins--within the brain. This validates classical Vedic philosophy, which describes the blissful, euphoric and elevated states of awareness in deep meditation.

But imagine having both sides working full-time, contributing 100% of their effort! Empirically speaking, the average human being only utilizes a mere 15% of their daily brainpower. To increase the percentile of brain activity, the two halves of the brain need to be synchronized, but most people are lateralized and fragmented in their thinking.

Greater synchronization between the right and left hemispheres as seen in long-term meditators has been associated with greater creativity and flexibility of thought. The whole process of meditation is about stilling the mind and relinquishing the thought process.

In a meditative state, our breathing becomes extremely slow, and activity in the heart is so synchronized that it creates a resonant vibrational link between the heart and the brain. According to Bentov, a circulating current in the sensory motor cortex of the brain is gradually established when we continue to meditate over time. This in turn releases old stresses locked into the brain tissue itself. The establishment of new neural pathways prevents the re-accumulation of stress effects, and actually stimulates the pleasure centers instead.

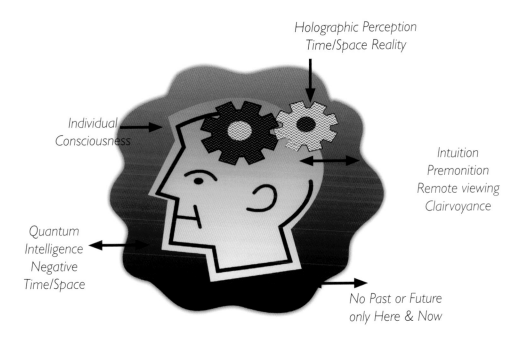

Holographic Perception
Time/Space Reality

Individual
Consciousness

Intuition
Premonition
Remote viewing
Clairvoyance

Quantum
Intelligence
Negative
Time/Space

No Past or Future
only Here & Now

Besides being responsible for changes in the neural pathways, meditation activates and helps unblock the *chakra* dysfunction, hence reducing the potential for manifesting disease and decreasing the intensity of any pre-existing illness. By mending the broken wheels, meditation thus provides emotional and physical immunity.

Long term meditators demonstrate far greater coherence of brain wave activity between the right and left cerebral hemispheres than non-meditators. If both sides of our brain are equally balanced, then our consciousness can experience transcendence. In deep meditation one enters the field of quantum intelligence where there is no past or future, only here and now.

The vehicle of meditation, and perhaps music drives our consciousness from everyday fixed time and space toward a more open vista--timeless, boundless reality. Only when we tune out the external world and its surroundings are we completely focused on and responsive to our 'inner world'--that part of us which is constantly refined by meditation.

Mind-Thought Illusion

A thought is always about something. It is totally dependent. It only appears when one becomes conscious of an event, theme, emotion or memory. Therefore a thought equals an object/event plus Consciousness. It ceases to exist when the object, event, theme or emotion is withdrawn. Hence, Consciousness equals a thought minus its content.

Try the following experiment. Please close your eyes and think, but make sure that your thought has no object, event, theme or emotion involved. Think about *nothing*. You will become *thought-less* and experience the underlying presence of Consciousness.

A thought appears only when one becomes conscious of an object, an event , a theme or an emotion.

A thought ceases to exist without an object, an event, a theme or an emotion

Thought = Object/Event + Consciousness

Consciousness = Thought - Object/Event

Karmic Footprints

Spirit and Matter

The body is like a chariot of which the soul is the owner; the intelligence is its driver, the mind plays the part of the reins; as for the horses, those are the senses; the world is their arena.

--Katha Upanishad

As humans, we are composed of both matter –our body, intellect and mind – as well as Spirit, our divine Self, or *Atman*, as it's known in the Vedic tradition. Matter in and of itself is inert –without life. Only when the inanimate matter merges with the spirit of the Self, a scintillating expression of life emerges.

The body-mind-intellect is matter. Matter is inert, insentient. But, when it comes into contact with the Self it becomes a living being. This is a phenomenon similar to an electric bulb glowing. The bulb has no light in and of itself. Nor does the electricity. But when the bulb is in contact with the electricity there is a brilliant expression of light.

Our physical body is home to the organs of perception and action, which gather stimuli from the external world. Our gross body is stimulated in various ways: sights and sounds, tastes and smells, and textures. For every stimulus of action the world provides, it is our physical body, which offers the reaction.

The mind and intellect react when they encounter stimuli. The mind processes and the intellect makes the decision. Our organs of actions emit responses back into the world. If the mind reacts to the stimuli without consulting or filtering them through intellect, the results are reactions that can, at best, be described as impulsive and at worst be perceived as insane. When the intellect filters such impetus, the reactions are objective and discrete. The responses, in a word, are mature.

For every action the external world offers, our body counters with a reaction through the enabling and enlivening power of the Self, or *Atman*. Without the presence of the Pure Consciousness vitalizing our body to react, mind to feel, and our intellect to think, our physical body would be but a mere mass of matter.

When we talk about the physical housing of our divine Self, we refer to it as 'my body, my mind, and my intellect.' Notice the use of 'my' – a possessive pronoun – indicates two aspects of our beliefs and thinking. It indicates that there exists something to be possessed as well as an individual to possess it.

We are the 'possessor'; the body-mind-intellect is the possession. If we possess the body-mind-intellect, then these parts cannot be 'we.' Then who exactly are we? In other words, if the body-mind-intellect were taken aware from our personality, there appears to be nothing left. Yet, still there is a feeling some unknown 'someone' is then claiming them as possessions. This 'someone', which claims them is *Atman*, the Self within.

Closely examine how we view your gross body and our workings. We watch our physical housing as it changes. As a youth, we studied it as the body grew taller; we observed as we gained knowledge. As we mature, we look in the mirror as our hair grays, our body gains or lose weight and as wrinkles appear.

We would not – indeed could not – observe these changes were there not some 'changeless entity' which is actually doing the observing. Observations of changes are only possible, scientists explain, when there is a fixed point of reference. In other words, a 'changeless factor' must be present which is performing the art of observation.

Compare this to the movement of a boat at 15 miles per hour. As a passenger on the boat, we only realize we are moving as we see the immovable objects on the shore whizzing past us. As we travel in an airplane, by contrast, our movement is not perceptible on a cloudless day because there are no clouds to use as points of reference.

Yet another compelling piece of evidence of an external Being is the use of the world 'I'. Every one of us uses this pronoun quite freely. 'I' is the one constant that spans our whole life. We use the pronoun 'I' to describe our experiences with all our senses. 'I see, hear, touch.' This use even extends to our dream state –'I dream' – and the deep-sleep phase – 'I am nothing.' The 'I' pervades all three states of consciousness and every physical, emotional and intellectual experience. You get up in the morning and say, 'I had a good night's sleep.' That which is ever awake and observes you while sleeping is the Pure Self.

Children watch enthralled by marionette puppets, not realizing that the puppets are connected to strings, controlled by the puppet master. As children mature, though, they are able to spot the wires, but still fail to recognize the ultimate controlling factor of the marionette. As they grow into adults, they understand and appreciate the unseen hands of the puppet master.

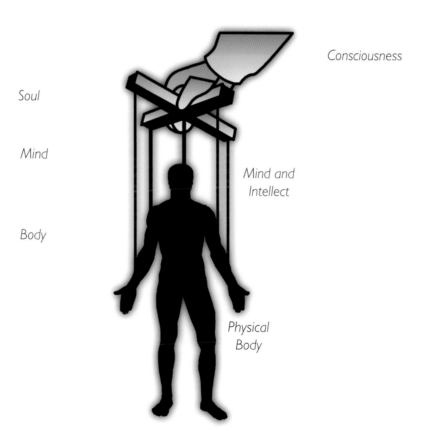

Similarly, those who have not fully evolved spiritually take the external manifested world and their gross body's actions as the main actors on the stage. They fail to realize that the overt actions of our physical self are really controlled by the inner strings of the mind and intellect, influencing our bodies. Those with spiritual insight understand, however, there exists a divine unseen puppeteer who watches and guides our actions and reactions.

Mind-Intellect

As the mind, so is the person.

In other words, the mind is the individual. If the mind is disturbed, so is the person. If the mind is calm, the person is calm.

The mind contains two distinct parts. The portion of the mind facing and receiving stimuli from the brain is the objective mind. The subjective or the intellect portion, in contrast, faces inwards and reacts to the stimuli received through the objective mind. This half is called the intellect.

Under the most ideal situation these two halves work in conjunction with each other. The intellect – the subjective portion – disciplines the objective or the mind prior to taking any action. Unfortunately, except for a very few individuals, the two halves of the mind in most people work along more independent lines. We have minds that are effectively split.

What creates this polarized condition? A layer of egoistic desires. In fact, the greater the ego, the larger the gap between the two parts of the mind become. In turn, the confusion within the individual increases and exhibits stronger desires for the material objects in life.

The task of the subjective mind is to filter thousands of stimuli, which reach us during the course of a day. We experience this through the five 'gateways of knowledge' – our organs of perception. The stimuli that react with our sense organs – our receptors – create impulses that bore through the objective mind. These impulses then filter deep down to the subjective layer through the intervening layers of individual egocentric desires.

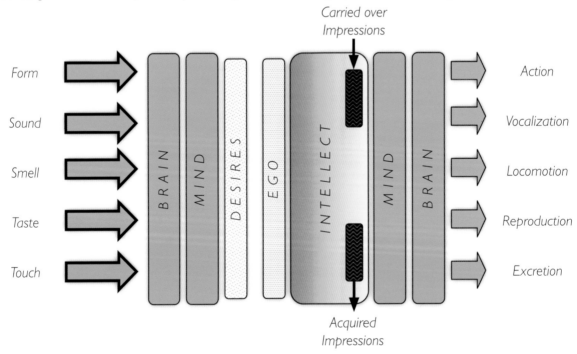

These impulses react with the existing impression of a person's own past actions that are already carefully stored in the subjective layer. They are then released back in the external world through the five organs of actions: hands, speech, feet, sex organs, and rectum. We call these our five active senses.

Every moment of every day, we meet different patterns of stimuli. In doing so, we gather new impressions in the subjective mind. Each set of impulses that reach the subjective mind not only adds to the ones already present, but also gets colored by the quality of the *vasanas* hoarded within. When the impressions are then translated into action, they are clouded by the existing *vasanas* in the subjective mind.

We all live under constant bombardment of a large variety of experiences. With each experience, we go through the process of perceiving, reacting with the perceived and eventually come to act in the outer field. During this process, we unwittingly cloud our thinking with an ever-increasing amount of 'dirt' of new impressions.

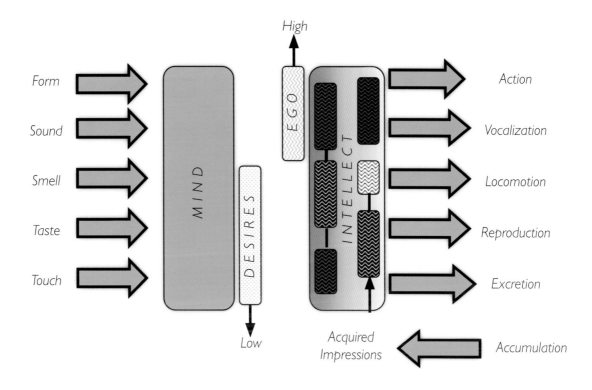

It's not surprising then that the 'subjective mind' increasingly gets covered with overlapping signatures of our own past moments. It's as if the mind builds layers of clouds between it and the spiritual Divinity. This prevents it from shining as the Pure Consciousness that resides deep within the core of our personality.

The Vedic wisdom emphasizes that reducing the *vasanas* is the means for purifying the mind. If you look into the mirror and cannot see your face, the problem is not because the mirror is defective. The difficulty arises because the image is covered because the mirror has a thick layer of dust on it obscuring your image.

To solve this problem, you would get a towel and wipe it clean. Then you are able to see your reflection. But wiping the mirror does not create the reflection it only unveils it. Similarly, a person is not aware of his divine nature because the 'subjective mind' keeps his inner mirror dull, coated with *vasanas* garnered during its egocentric, passionate existence in the world.

Only by removing that thick layer of dust which clouds our true vision, can we bring the subjective and objective aspects of the mind together. It is only then that the objective mind is discipline well enough to act faithfully under the guidance of the subjective mind.

The result of this true reflection and working partnership of the two aspects of the mind is simple, yet spectacular. This can only be accomplished by the removal of the dividing factor of egocentric desires.

Once the union takes place, one becomes skilled in this reconciliation. Then – and only then – does the objective mind react intelligently and faithfully to external stimuli. Actions become more thoughtful and the purging of the already existing *vasanas* begins.

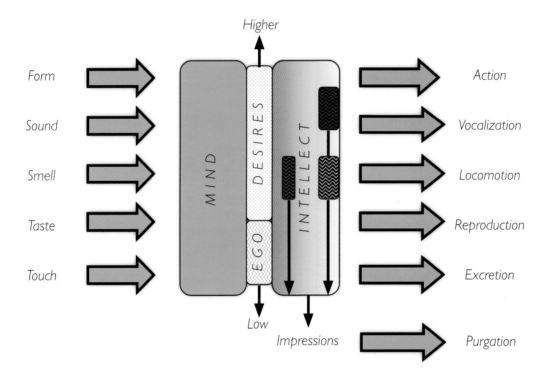

Viewed spiritually, the subjective mind is our secret weapon. This is an outlet for the existing impressions that have been accumulated for years. The average person, however, misuses this dangerous weapon to prompt his own destruction. All too often, it is used as an inlet, which creates a new supply of mental impressions through his selfish activities and low motives.

Nature, though, provides new equipments – bodies – that will eventually exhaust these impressions. Each new body houses the same ego, life after life. The message of the *Vedas* explains that actions are not to be avoided and the world of objects is not to be denied. Only by making intelligent use of these impressions can they provide us with a field for exhausting our mental dirt.

The core of our personality is the supreme Self, or *Atman*. It is responsible for the ability of the physical body to perceive outside stimuli as well as for the mind to feel. The quality of perceptions, of actions, feelings and thoughts coming from your body, and intellect depends on your inherent nature, or *vasanas*. If our *vasanas*, our basic nature, is good, then our expressions will be good. If our *vasanas* are bad, then it follows our expression will be bad.

In the chronology of an action *vasana* comes first, next thought, desire and then action. *Vasanas*, when not manifest, remain dormant in us as our potential nature. They are in that state when we are in deep sleep. When they begin to manifest themselves they first appear as thoughts in our intellect. In the next phase, *vasanas* express desires in our mind. If given importance, the desire culminates in the physical body as action.

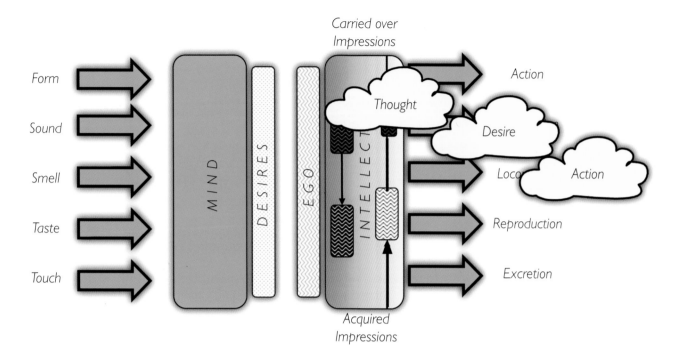

The human physical personality has two parts: the perceiver and the actor. When the *Atman* operates through the organs of perception, it becomes the perceiver. The *Atman* receives the colors and shapes, sounds, taste and touch. The perceiver, therefore, is the combined seer-hearer-smeller-taster-toucher.

When the *Atman* functions through the organs of action it is the actor. The actor, naturally enough, initiates your physical actions. In the same vein, when the *Atman* operates through the mind, it becomes the feeler. It feels all the emotions that are available in the world: joy, sorrow, love, hate, passion, anger and affection to name just a few. The feeler is the emotional personality.

The third component of the human personality is the intellect, which itself is divided into the gross and the subtle. Each part plays a distinctly different role. The gross intellect is the discriminating faculty with which we distinguish pairs of opposites. Our gross intellect tells us the difference between hot and cold, joy and sorrow, right and wrong. This component grapples with the profound themes of science and technology as well. Through the gross intellect, the *Atman* becomes the thinker, and conceives thoughts that relate to the world.

The subtle intellect, in contrast, separates the transcendental from the worldly. It is the half of our intellect which thinks of the possibility of the eternal Reality which extends beyond the ephemeral world. Through the subtle intellect, the *Atman* discerns Spirit from matter and is known as the contemplator.

The Pure Consciousness, or *Atman*, operates through the body to come conscious of perception and action, through the mind to become conscious of emotion and through the intellect to become conscious of thought.

The physical body conditions the Pure Consciousness through our unintelligent identification and attachment to our body, mind and spirit. We are, in effect, a hostage to our perception and action, emotion and thought.

When, as a seeker of spiritual knowledge, we rise above your physical filters and traverse beyond these limitations, the conditioner disappears. The veil of individuality lifts. The spiritual seeker merges with the pure, absolute Consciousness. It is similar to the phenomenon of reflection and sunlight. Remove the reflecting medium and the reflected image disappears. But the all-pervading sunlight remains.

Anatomy of Desire

The way that can be spoken of is not the constant way;
The name that can be named is not the constant name.
The nameless was the beginning of heaven and earth;
The named was the mother of the myriad creatures.
Hence always rid yourself of desires in order to observe its secrets;
But always allow yourself to have desires in order to observe its manifestations.
These two are the same but diverge in name as they issue forth.
Being the same they are called mysteries, mystery upon mystery - the gateway of the manifold secrets.

- Lao Tsu / The Tao Te Ching - translated D.C Lau

A primitive urge, when stimulated, generates emotional energy. Channeling this energy toward a specific goal then becomes a desire to fulfill an urge. All desire is nothing but the fulfilling of emotional energy for repeat pleasure or avoidance of pain.

As long as we have physical bodies, we have desires. In and of themselves, desires are not destructive. It is the quality and quantity of them that causes our distress and dissatisfaction with life.

A person whose sole motivation is prompted by one of the four primary urges – food, fear, sex and sleep – exhibits animalistic desires. These are the same drives that are instinctive in animals and usually remain undirected. Animals have no reasoning power and are dominated by theses urges.

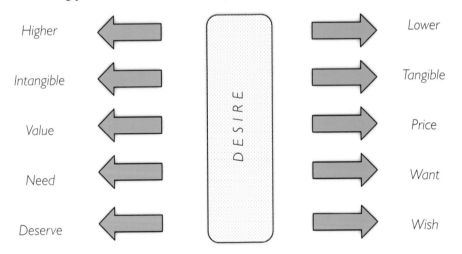

Similarly, we experience an urge when we fear for our lives, feel starved, exhausted or are sexually attracted to another. But human intelligence has evolved beyond these instinctual habits. As a species, we possess the power of cognitive reasoning and the will of discernment. Yet many people still act solely out of these lower impulses. These four urges are also associated with the three lower *chakras* of the body: the root, sacral, and the navel.

The fulfillment of these lower-level desires may bring a person transient happiness, but provide no long-lasting satisfaction in a person's life. What's more, the moment one is satisfied, the dissatisfaction begins. Primitive urges usually fall into the category of items that are tangible. The constant collecting of 'stuff' – material items, such as clothes, jewelry, or even money --is based on the lower, primitive urges.

Desires can also be directed toward the higher, intangible items of life, music and other creative ventures. Most of these desires are derived from carried over karmic impressions of past lives.

How we fulfill our desires speaks volumes not only about us, but how we view the world around us. For example, in choosing between two items – material or nonmaterial – it is always a better to select the one that has more value, not necessarily the more expensive article. What, after all, is the value of a glass of water if one were dying of thirst?

Many people fail to recognize the difference between a need and the mere yearning or wanting of items. Food, clothing, shelter, education, transportation and freedom to follow your own belief system are considered needs. Wants, on the other hand, only prompt discontent in your life.

Finally, desires are not fulfilled merely because they wish them to be. Wishing something so has never produced results. Wishing for a college education without putting forth any effort toward that goal – applying for college, financial aid, or any other necessary step – will not materialize into an education. One only gets what one deserves and not what one desires.

Anatomy of Ego

The ego often serves as the source of mental afflictions and emotional troubles. The ego, or 'CEO', regularly forgets that the real head of the body is the pure Self. The ego takes pleasure, so it seems, in running the company according to its own rules with little regard to anything else.

Directly derived from the intellect, the ego handpicks what it likes and dislikes in the world, making the necessary arrangements with the memory banks. An entirely thought-bound entity, the ego is conditioned by the need to preserve its own pseudo-existence.

If a person wants to be considered by others as intelligent, for example our ego-self will seek out situations and relationships in which we appear superior. Similarly, a person who is more concerned about his physical appearance finds that the ego places him in situations in which he will outshine others.

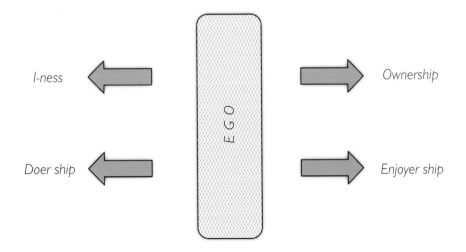

Our mind, very often, is compared to a computer. To continue with this analogy, the ego would be the self-perpetuating 'virus.' It believes that it is the most important part of the human system and organizes any incoming data to suit its arguments for actions.

If a person possesses a combination of large ego with the domination of the lower, instinctual desires, then there exists disharmony in the mind and intellect. This creates havoc and pain within a person. His actions and perceptions work in this case to create karmic footprints – impressions that cloud his view of his pure Self.

By contrast, if one can tame his ego, and diligently fulfill the more intangible desires, harmony is produced within the mind. The pursuit of these desires, additionally, promotes the purgation of accumulated karmic impressions from previous lifetimes as well as any from this life.

Karma

There is the path of joy and there is the path of pleasure, both attract the soul. The two paths lie in front of man. Pondering on them, the wise chooses the path of joy: the fool takes the path of pleasure.

--Katha Upanishad

There are two natural laws at work in our lives: destiny and karma.

Each of us is the product of a cumulative effect of our past thoughts, desires and action. It's a classic example of cause and effect. Your past activities are the cause; your present personality is the effect. Your destiny at any given time is the result of your past actions and choices. These cannot be changed. You need to accept the result of these 'causes.' Your present destiny, therefore, is set. Destiny controls your action up to the present moment.

But that is only one of the laws, which work in your life. It is the law of destiny, which defines you as the product of your accumulative experiences up until this present moment. It essentially identifies with your past. Your present moments and your future, however, are governed by a different law. Your future is affected by the law of karma. In effect, it is an extension of the law of destiny into the future. The law of karma explains that in addition to being the product of your past, you are the producer of your present and future as well.

Look ahead to your future with optimism. With the law of karma, you realize that even though your difficulties and shortcomings created your past, you now have the opportunity to create a brighter, more successful future – however you choose to define success. You, indeed, are the master of your karma.

A person is identified with his past while at the same time he is free to act as he wills in the present moment and beyond. In the Vedic tradition, the law of destiny is known as *prarabdha*. The law of karma is *purushartha*. Whatever the nature and quality of your past efforts are reflected in your present destiny.

Many people refuse to see the difference in these two related laws. They wrongly assume that if their past has been filled with negativity or failure that their future must be dictated by the same influences. They also mistakenly believe that if their actions have been positive and spiritual up until the present, then they are 'destined' to continue on this path.

Very often this does happen, if for no other reason, this is the path of least resistance. Psychologists would say that we tend to continue in our 'comfort zone,' until some major stimulus pushes us beyond it. We continue to be who and what we always have been, merely because it is the easiest route to take. But that is not to say we cannot change.

Let's compare the flow of your life to a speed boat on a river. Your 'boat' moves at 15 miles per hour. That's a constant speed in quiet waters. The river though is moving at a rate of 5 miles per hour. When the boat travels downstream then the speed is 20 miles per hour –the speed of the vessel, 15 mph, added to the downstream pull of the river, 5 mph.

This is the speed of your life if you 'go with the flow' of your current destiny, all the actions and experiences that have made you who you are today.

Continuing with this analogy, let's say you've made a consciousness decision to change your life. This is not impossible because your future actions are not dictated by your past, thanks to the law of karma. But it does mean that the boat will be traveling against the flow of the current. You boat is now moving upstream, but at a slower rate than had it been continuing in the direction it had been. Your 15 mph is reduced by 5 mph because of this. You may be only traveling 10 mph, but you are gaining so much during this effort. Along the way you'll be acquiring new habits and attitudes.

Destiny cannot be changed. The future, though, can be created through the power of free will and self-effort. The 'total karma' is only determined at the time of death.

Action Reaction

For every action there is an equal and opposite reaction.

--Newton's third law of motion

Interestingly, that same law is the essence of the Law of Karma. For every action we perform there exists an equal and opposite reaction. The only difference between the two laws is in the length of time for the 'reaction' to occur.

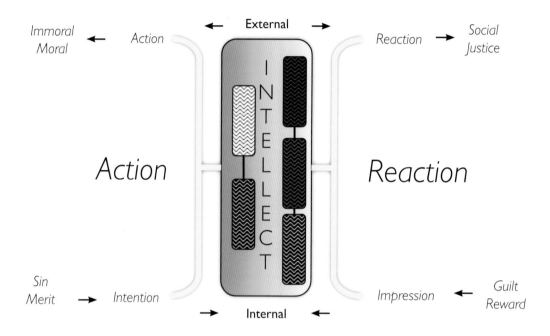

Newton's law refers to physicals objects. Each action produces a reaction that is visible and identifiable. A good example of Newton's law is a game of billiards. When the cue ball hits another ball, the second ball reactions by moving forward on its own path.

For every action a person performs – good or bad – there exists a reaction to that. It is similar to the Biblical adage that 'you reap what you sow'. Karma contains within in two parts: one visible, one invisible.

The visible portion of the Karmic law is quite obvious. A person shoots another and receives a jail sentence. Action: the shooting. Reaction: punishment.

It is not the action itself that causes the reaction, but it is the *intention* behind the action that causes an impression. For example, a husband may ask his wife for a glass of water. The wife gets him the water, but grudgingly, mumbling to herself, 'The lazy good-for-nothing. He can't even get up and get his own glass of water.' Even though the wife performed an act of kindness, the *intention* behind it was not at all charitable. The reaction would be the creation of a karmic impression that would need to be purged either in this or another lifetime. The wife would not 'sow' kindness in spite of her compliance with the request.

Carried-Over Karma

Think of carried-over Karma as Divine Justice. The Law of Karma asserts that every person reaps what he sows, if not in this lifetime, then the next – or even the one after that.

A person's deeds in a lifetime can either be guided by of virtue or vice. The deeds can help lift up another person, even in a small way, or they can be injurious and harmful to either one or more people. If the actions are of a harmful nature, they leave karmic impressions that will eventually need to be purged.

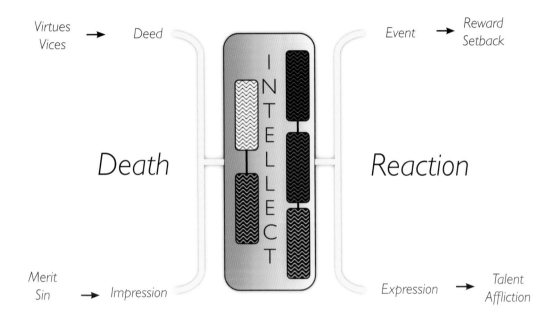

For example, if a person intentionally blinds another, the karmic impression left will eventually be revealed in the form of blindness. That does not mean, however, the person inflicting the blindness will go blind himself within his present life span. He could be born in his next reincarnation as blind, or acquire blindness in his next lifetime.

That is carried-over karma. In fact, let's take this analogy one step further. Let's say the person who inflicted intentional blindness on another was an eye doctor in a previous lifetime. His past virtuous deeds included giving many people sight. He would not 'pay' for his action in this lifetime, then, because his past actions accumulated an enormous amount of 'light potential' for his eyesight. It is not until his vices have exhausted his virtues that he will experience blindness. Karma can be thought of as a 'bank account.' You accumulate credit in one lifetime and carry over your account into the next.

At the time of a person's physical death, the karmic impressions left by the injurious deeds he has performed stay with his subtle body. When he is reborn in another lifetime, these karmic impressions may appear either as affliction at birth or acquired illnesses, ailments as he ages.

Similarly, when a person physically dies, his accumulated merits, or good deeds, stay with the subtle body. Born into the next lifetime, these may gain expression either as talents that are unexplainable – such as in child protégées – or in unusually 'good luck' and rewards as he lives his life.

The unexplained and stunning talent of Mozart were exhibited as young as the age five. It is only but one of the examples in this world of an accumulation of good deeds transforming into an intangible desire and manifesting into a remarkable, apparently unexplainable talent.

How can such karma be kept from one life to the next? At the time of a person's death, the physical body dies, but the subtle body, as we discussed, does not. It transmigrates and comes to a quintessence. The subtle body is the residence of our karmic impressions – those deeds we performed, not just in the last life, but in all our appearances. These deeds are a mixture of both good and bad. In some, the bad karma outweighs the good; in others, the lofty and noble deeds outnumber the bad.

Once our bodies come back into physicality, along with our carried-over karmic impressions, we receive another opportunity to work at eradicating the bad, expanding on the good, and continue working toward our ultimate destination: the revelation of the unseen but ever-present Pure Consciousness.

Divine Justice is not limited to merely one lifetime, therefore. It has an eternal, infallible memory.

No soul escapes Divine Justice.

Karmic Cycle

While this body is yet free of disease and
the old age is yet far away
while the strength in the senses yet waxes and
the lifespan is not in ebb,
the wise man must right now undertake
endeavors for spiritual uplifting
for, what effort to dig a well
when the house is already on fire.

-- *Puranas,* ancient Hindu Scripture

All memories of our previous lives are removed from our consciousness shortly after birth. This 'built-in' amnesia allows each of us to develop and grow according to the new environments without the contaminating influence of knowledge or habits acquired in previous lives.

Each individual personality of a physical incarnation is actually a fragment of the one single greater soul, also known as the higher spiritual Self.

The total soul is a collective consciousness of many individual incarnations or personalities whose knowledge and experience are woven together like a colorful tapestry. Each individual soul increases its understanding of its emotional capacity, creativity, its intellectual abilities as well recognizes its physical limitations. These experiences differ for each personality. The ultimate goal, however, is the same for each soul: to grow in a greater awareness of its own higher spiritual nature.

This cycle of reincarnation possesses specific safeguards built into it to prevent the perpetuation of improper thinking and negative actions on others pursing the same journey of self discovery and enlightenment. This system – the Law of Karma – is what leaves the impressions of our past lives on our present. We could even view the karmic footprints as energy debits and credits based on past positive and negative deeds.

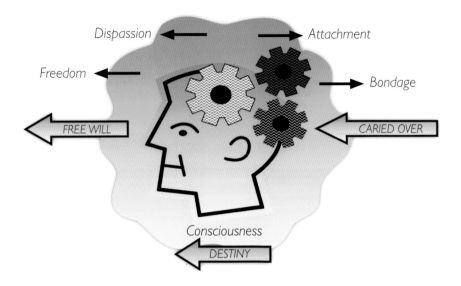

The subtle nature of our higher dimensional anatomy allow the negative energies to be carried over to future life times through abnormalities in the physical and emotional structure.

By working through physical handicaps and illnesses individuals are able to erase the karmic footprints of negative deeds. Individuals also receive opportunity to redeem their souls for the evils, torments and suffering they may have caused others in previous lives. Often the ways people have injured others come to haunt them in their future lives in a manner that is symbolically reminiscent of the original harmful act.

Consider the person whose past lives included one in which he participated in the Spanish inquisition. He blinded people accused of heresy with a red hot iron sword in that life. In a later life, this individual may develop an incurable form of blindness.

The nature of this type of karmic expression allows the tormentor to eventually understand the true nature of the suffering he inflicted on another person. He also learns, from this experience, to overcome obstacles and handicaps. This helps the person grow stronger in the face of adversity.

The accumulated impressions of a person lead to another life in which the person returns and makes amends in order to erase the impressions of his previous – as well as his present – lives. An abundance of negative impressions generates the appearance of lower, ego-driven desires in his present life. These desires include anger, greed, attachment, selfishness, and passion. The result of these ego-driven desires is a life of bondage and attachment, requiring numerous lifetimes to correct. But the truly sad fact is that while the soul is toiling at these baser, more animalistic desires, it is not working on its chance to clear the impressions of previously carried-over karmic content, and thus delaying the liberation for many lifetimes.

A life carrying fewer impressions and fewer negative deeds in this life will soon find that freedom from karma is at hand. This person will discover that he is able to work with a sense of dispassion, compassion, charity, detachment, and selflessness. He epitomizes the adage by which every soul needs to live: 'Do your best and leave the rest.'

A person's attempt to clear the few impressions his soul is carrying will discover that the law of destiny – those events in his past that he cannot change – hold less control over his life. This person concentrates more on the law of karma –seizing control of his future and creating a life that is characterized by self-effort, freedom and the exhibition of free will.

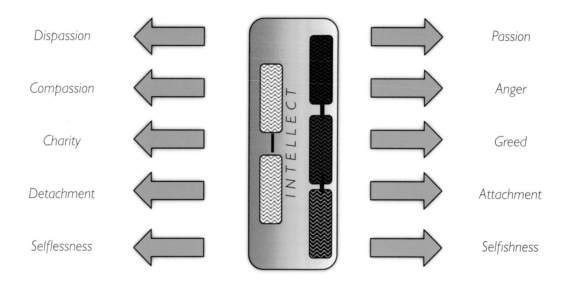

This takes the individual on an exceptional journey that pushes him closer to his higher self. The fewer the karmic impressions an individual is born with, the closer he travels to true enlightenment. This type of life leads towards a choice of even reincarnating another time. The individual will have no desire to return to another life on earth, as there will be no need—there is no karmic impression with which to contend. The person's lifting of impressions allows the Pure Consciousness, the substratum, of the universe to shine within him. This is true freedom.

The Highest Secret

Then you are not experiencing -- an experience. Not observing – an object observed. But you know yourself to be that light which is as though a thousand Suns have risen simultaneously in the sky. All the colors of the universe shine in you. A thousand Suns shine in what you call the moment in you, but in that moment you know that to be yourself. You know yourself to be that.

--Swami Veda Bharati

The *Gayatri Mantra.*

Among the literally millions of sacred sound formulas archived in the Far East, this one is universally considered the essence of all *mantras.* All spiritual powers and potencies are contained within it. The *Gayatri Mantra* is recognized throughout India and the Himalayas as supreme for achieving enlightenment. Indeed, amid the diversity of practices in both Hinduism and Buddhism, it is universally practiced.

This sacred *mantra* appears in the *Rig Veda, Yajur Veda,* and *Sama Veda,* the earliest of the Hindu scriptures. Its origins can be traced to a sage named Vishwamitra, a king who renounced his throne to seek spiritual awakening. He was the first to realize the essence of the luminous spheres of creation through this *mantra.* Now, several thousands years later, his gift continues to free countless spiritual seekers.

The essence of the universe is in the three *Vedas*, the essence of the *Vedas* is in the three segments of the *Gayatri*, and the essence of the *Gayatri* is in three words, *Bhuh, Bhuvah, Swaha*. These three words are an addition to the *Gayatri Mantra*. Called the *maha-vyahrtis*, they are the great utterances of the Lord. The word *maha*, most closely translated to the Greek 'mega,' means the great. And *vyahrtis* means an 'utterance.' The three great utterances are the *maha-vyahrtis*.

A-U-M contains the essence of the *maha-vyahrtis*. Whatever applies to A applies to *Bhuh* and to the first segment of *Gayatri*. Whatever applies to the sound U, applies to the sound, mega-utterance *Bhuvah*, and the second segment of the *Gayatri*. And whatever applies to the sound M, applies to the sound *Swaha* and to the third segment of the *Gayatri*.

These words are an expansion. In *mantra* science, a central sound is a *bija*, a seed. Its expansion is the fruit, and the tree and the branches. *Gayatri* has been regarded, next to Om, as the most powerful *mantra* and called the Mother of the *Vedas*. Om is the sound.

Gayatri is the central *mantra* of the solar science, a science of hidden energies. Its essence is two-fold; the Sun, and Beauty; the knowledge of the Sun that dwells within you, with which you establish and discover your identity, and beauty.

The *Vedas* teach the entire cosmos is composed of vibration. The galaxies, suns, planets, ether, molecules, atoms and even you and I are all made of vibration. Achieving spiritual advancement is refining our level of vibration. Seeking enlightenment is the act of seeking the universal source of vibration.

There are seven *lokas* or luminous spheres of light, according to Vedic cosmology. Each successive sphere is more spiritually advanced and sublime than the previous one. The upper realms of light are the abodes of saints and sages, prophets and rishis, angels and archangels. Each *loka*, *Veda* tradition tells us, can be summarized in a single vibration, which can be invoked by a syllable. Intoning the syllable brings the vibration of that particular sphere into oneself. The Sanskrit words of the *Gayatri Mantra* contain the essential vibration of all seven *lokas*.

Two renditions of the *Gayatri Mantra* exist. The long form is as follows:

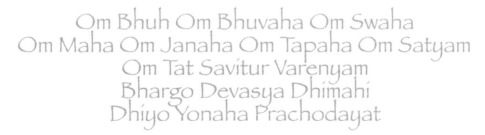

Om Bhuh Om Bhuvaha Om Swaha
Om Maha Om Janaha Om Tapaha Om Satyam
Om Tat Savitur Varenyam
Bhargo Devasya Dhimahi
Dhiyo Yonaha Prachodayat

'O self-effulgent light that has given birth to all the *lokas*, who is worthy of worship and appears through the orbit of the Sun, illumine our intellect.'

This powerful chant invokes the spiritual planes – and any associated physical *chakras*. The correlation between the spiritual plane and the physical *chakras* are indicated below:

Om Bhuh – Earth plane (first *chakra*)

Om Bhuvaha – atmospheric plane (second *chakra*)

Om Swaha – solar region (third *chakra*)

Om Maha – first spiritual region beyond the Sun; heart vibration (fourth *chakra*)

Om Janaha – second spiritual region beyond the Sun; power of the divine spiritual Word (fifth *chakra*)

Om Tapaha – third spiritual region beyond the Sun; sphere of the progenitors (sixth *chakra*) (This sphere represents the highest realm of spiritual understanding a person can attain while still being identified with individual existence.)

Om Satyam – the abode of supreme Truth; absorption into the Supreme (seventh *chakra*)

Om Tat Savitur Varenyam – that realm of Truth that is beyond human comprehension (-- the essence of *Rig Veda*)

Bhargo Devasya Dhimahi (-- the essence of *Yajur Veda*)

Dhiyo Yonaha Prachodayat (-- the essence of *Sama Veda*)

'In that place where all the celestials of all the spheres have received enlightenment, kindly enlighten our intellect.'

The ultimate goal of all spiritual discipline, including the practice of reciting the Sanskrit *mantra*, is the realization of a higher or the 'ideal state' of being. The ideal state is spiritual being can be interpreted in a number of ways, depending on your goals. This, indeed, is your personal choice. You may decide you want to change your destiny. You may endeavor to be a 'good' spiritual' or a righteous person. Or you may wish to attain union with a great spiritual figure, to be one with the body of Christ, to be in union with Krishna forever.

Gayatri is a purificatory *mantra*. Purification means to remove karmic impressions. It also leads to break through into short-cuts into wisdom. Wisdom means self-knowledge. Knowing that you are a spiritual entity, the cosmic light and sound is the only source of knowledge, the only source of wisdom. When you are doing the *mantra*, all layers of meaning of those words should be experienced simultaneously, not as a translation, but as a feeling.

Those select few who follow through on these intentions ultimately will determine the fate of humanity. Look deep within yourself and identify your own spiritual ideal. Dedicate all of your spiritual practices and disciplines toward this apex of achievement. You need not forgo intermediate goals such as wealth, a satisfying marriage, a fulfilling job or even good health. Practicing this *mantra* means you have framed an ultimate destination based on your own nature as a spiritual being.

Below is the short version of this highest *Secret of Reality*:

Om Bhuh, Bhuvaha, Swaha
Om Tat Savitur Varenyam
Bhargo Devasya Dhimahi
Dhiyo Yonaha Prachodayat

'I meditate on the radiant and most venerable light of the Divine, from which issues forth the triple world (the *Bhuh*, *Bhuvah*, and *Swaha*). May the divine light illuminate and guide my intellect.'

This is the sound that the light makes when it travels …

Secrets

- Consciousness is ever evolving. Transpersonal awareness is the hopeful destination.

- Consciousness is the only Reality. Matter is an illusion created by the mind.

- Holographic model of Consciousness explains the nature of collective consciousness.

- Entrainment of consciousness is the principle at work for the repetition of mantras, chants, and the effectiveness of prayers.

- The cycle of consciousness revolves around the three conditioned states: awake, dream and deep sleep.

- The unconditioned state of Pure Consciousness is called turiya, or the fourth state.

- At death, the entire content of consciousness comes to a quintessence before transmigrating.

- Chakras are specialized centers of consciousness, which transform higher energies into a lower form that the body can use.

- Chakras and nadis are part of our unseen connection between the Spirit and matter.

- Our wellness or illness depends upon the function and dysfunction of the chakras respectively.

- Our physical self responds to subtle transitions in our awareness through the workings of the autonomic nervous system.

- Human perception is not located at any specific site within the physical brain.

- Holograms and Fourier Transforms provide new ways of understanding how the brain perceives and stores information.

- The stored impressions or vasanas – unique to the individual observer – interfere and thus alter perception.

- *Consciousness, at its most basic, is coherent light.*

- *Mind is nothing but a chain of thoughts. No thought, no mind.*

- *If there is no breath, there is no thought. Breath is the physical counterpart of the mind.*

- *A thought travels faster than the speed of light, hence supraluminal.*

- *It is not mind over matter; it is matter over matter.*

- *Dual thoughts are limiting and contract our awareness. Non-dual thoughts lead to synchronization of the two brain hemispheres.*

- *A thought is always about an object, event, theme or an emotion.*

- *The body – mind – intellect is inert matter. Only when it comes in contact with the Self, it becomes a living being.*

- *The ego, or 'CEO', regularly forgets that the real President of the body is the pure Self.*

- *One cannot be desire-less but can choose higher and intangible desires.*

- *'As you sow, so shall you reap' is the law of cause and effect called Karma.*

- *It is the unseen intention behind an action that determines the resultant aquired impression or vasana.*

- *Destiny is the cumulative action up to the present. The future is determined by free will and self-effort. The 'total karma' is resolved only at the time of death.*

- *Attachment leads to bondage. Dispassion leads to freedom from the karmic cycle.*

- *The sacred Gayatri mantra is the highest secret for enlightenment.*

References

Al-Khalil, Jim. *Quantum, A Guide for the Perplexed.* (United Kingdom: Weidenfeld and Nicolson, 2003)

Arya, Pandit Usharbudh, D.Litt. *God.* (Pennsylvania: The Himalayan International Institute of Yoga Science and Philosophy, 1979)

Arya, Pandit Usharbudh, D.Litt. *Meditation And The Art Of Dying.* (Pennsylvania: The Himalayan International Institute of Yoga Science and Philosophy, 1985)

Barnes and Noble, Inc. *The Illustrated History of the World.* (Barnes and Noble Books, 2001)

Bentov, I. *'Micromotion of the Body as a Factor in the Development of the Nervous System,' in Kundalini: Evolution and Enlightenment,* ed. J. White (St. Paul, Minnesota: Athena Books, 1990)

Borges, Jorge Luis. *Other Inquisitions.* 1935-1952. (University of Texas Press. 1984)

Brain/Mind Bulletin. *Electronic Evidence of Auras, Chakras in UCLA Study.* (vol.3,no.9 March20,1978)

Burr, Harold. *The Fields of Life.* (New York : Ballantine Books,1972)

Briggs, J. and Peat, F. *'David Bohm's Looking-Glass Map,' in Looking Glass Universe: The Emerging Science of Wholeness.* (New York: Simon & Schuster, Inc., 1984)

Capra, Fritjof. *The Tao of Physics.* (New York: Bantam Books, 1988)

Dumitrescu, I. and Kenyon, J. *Electrographic Imaging in Medicine and Biology.* (Suffolk, Great Britain: Neville Spearman Ltd., 1983)

Flood, Gavin. *An Introduction to Hinduism.* (United Kingdom: Cambridge University Press, 1996)

Gerber, Richard. *Vibrational Medicine.* (New Mexico: Bear & Company, 2001)

Goswami, Amit, Ph.D. *The Self-Aware Universe.* (New York, Tarcher/Putnam, 1995)

Goswami, Amit, Ph.D. *Physics of the Soul.* (Virginia: Hampton Roads Publishing Company, Inc., 2001)

Greene, Brian. *The Elegant Universe.* (New York: Vintage Books, Random House, 2003)

Gribbin, John. *Quantum Physics.* (New York: DK Publishing, Inc., 2002)

Gribbin, John. *The Expanding Universe.* (New York: DK Publishing, Inc., 2002)

Hawking, Stephen. *A Brief History of Time.* (New York: Bantam Books, 1990)

Hodson, G. *The Miracle of Birth: A Clairvoyant Study of a Human Embryo.* (Wheaton, IL: Theosophical Publishing House, 1981)

Kapoor, Raj MD. *Mend the Mind, Mind the Body, Meet the Soul.* (Indiana: 1st Books Library, 2003)

Kirlian, S. & Kirlian, V. *Photography Visual Observations by Means of High Frequency Currents.* (Journal of Scientific and Applied Photography, vol.6, 1961)

Laszlo, Ervin. *Science and the Akashic Field.* (Rochester, Vermont: Inner Traditions, 2004)

McTaggart, Lynne. *The Field.* (New York: Harper Collins Publishers, 2002)

Moring, Gary F., M.A. *Theories of the Universe.* (Indiana: Alpha Books. 2002)

Moring, Gary F., M.A. *Understanding Einstein.* (Indiana: Alpha Books, 2002)

Motoyama, H. *Theories of the Chakras: Bridge to Higher Consciousness.* (Wheaton, IL: Theosophical Publishing House, 1981)

Oppenheimer, Julius Robert. *Science and the Common Understanding.* (The Reith Lectures. Unknown binding, 1901)

Parthasarathy, A. *The Eternities.* (Mumbai, India: Published by A. Parthasarathy, 2004)

Prigogine, I and Stengers, I. *Order Out Of Chaos: Man's New Dialogue With Nature.* (New York: Bantam Books, 1984)

Stevenson, Ian. *Where Reincarnation and Biology Intersect.* (Westport, Connecticut: Praeger Publishers, 1997)

Swami Rajarshi Muni. *Awakening Life Force.* (Minnesota: Llewellyn Publications, 1993)

Swami Chinmayananda. *The Holy Geeta.* (Mumbai: Central Chinmaya Mission Trust, 1992)

Talbot, Michael. *Beyond the Quantum.* (New York: Bantam books, 1986)

Talbot, Michael. *The Holographic Universe.* (New York: Harper-Perennial, 1992)

Talbot, Michael. *Mysticism and the New Physics.* (Middlesex, England: Penguin Group, 1993)

Tallack, Peter. *The Science Book.* (United Kingdom: Weidenfield and Nicolson, 2003)

Tiller, William. *Some Energy Field Observations of Man and Nature, in The Kirlian Aura,* ed. Krippner and Rubin (Garden City, NY: Anchor Press/Doubleday, 1974)

Tiller, William. *The Positive and Negative Space/Time Frames as Conjugate Systems, in Future Science,* ed. White and Krippner (Garden City, NY: Doubleday & Co., Inc.,1977)

Weiss, Brian. *Many Lives, Many Masters.* (New York: Fireside Book, Simon & Schuster Inc., 1988)

Index

A

Abdus Salam, 97

About Time, 7, 78

Absolute Self, 205

Action Reaction, 9, 236

Activator Repressor, 168-169

Active Senses, 132-134, 138, 149

Afterglow of Creation, 7, 88

Ahamkara, 133, 249

Alain Aspect, 47, 50

Albert Einstein, 32-33, 37, 39, 72, 83, 93

Aleksandr Oparin, 128

Aliveness, 7, 139-143, 147, 150, 198, 218

Allen Detrick, 135

Ananda, 118

Anatta, 161

Ancient Vedic Atomic Theory, 35

Anderson, 191

Andromeda Galaxy, 101

Antimatter, 59, 67, 89, 91

Antiparticle, 54, 59, 132

Archbishop James Ussher, 126

Archimedes, 20

Aristotle, 155

Arno Penzias, 88, 91

Arrow of Time, 7, 76, 79-80, 120

Arthur Stanley Eddington, 85

Aryan, 16

Aspect Experiment, 48-49

Atom, 6, 33-35, 38, 47, 54-55, 57, 66-67, 79, 88, 90, 95-96, 98, 130, 186, 221

Attachment, 110, 231, 239-240, 245

AUM, 195, 241

Avatara, 109

Avesta, 16

Awake State, 189, 194-195

Awareness, 7, 110, 117, 131, 133, 137, 139-143, 147, 150-153, 186-187, 189, 198, 202-203, 205-206, 218, 222, 238, 244-245

B

Basophils, 174-175

Benjamin Franklin, 150

Bentov, 186-187, 200, 223

Bernstein, 214

Beta, 156, 189, 222

Bhagavad Gita, 59

Bhaskara, 19

Bhuh, 241-242

Bhuvah, 241-242

Bhuvaha, 241-242

Bible, 126-127

Big Bang Theory, 90, 120

Big Crunch, 92, 160

Biocosm, 7, 125, 199

Bioenergetic Spectrum, 7, 139

Birth Mark, 156

Blastocyst, 146-147

Bliss, 106, 195-196, 202

Blockages, 205

Blueprint of Life, 8, 163

Bondage, 239, 245

Bosons, 56

Brahma, 112-113

Brahmagupta, 19

Brahmin, 21, 248

Breath, 131, 137, 141-142, 150, 217-219, 245

Brian Weiss, 156, 158

Buddha, 111, 161

Buddhism, 152, 161, 240

Burr, 134-136, 246

C

C. J. Ducasse, 156

Carl Jung, 190-191

Carl Sagan, 112, 114

Carlisle, 150

Carol Brown, 156

Carried-Over Karma, 9, 237

Causal Determinism, 27, 40

Causal Power, 62-64, 177

Causation, 62-63, 107, 109, 113, 118, 136, 140

Centers of Consciousness, 8, 203,

Itzhak Bentov, 186-187, 200

J

J. Krishnamurti, 49, 51
J. White, 246
Jacques Benveniste, 173-174, 176
Jalaluddin Rumi, 155
James Clerk Maxwell, 28
James Joyce, 57
James Watson, 165
JBS Haldane, 128
Jean B. J. Fourier, 214
Jesus Christ, 111, 127
Jews, 155
Johann Lambert, 20
John Bell, 46, 48, 50
John Wheeler, 81
Jorge Luis, 13, 246
Joseph J. Thompson, 33
Juan Oro, 129
Judgment Day, 155
Julius Robert, 62

K

Kali-Yuga, 113-114
Kalpa, 112-113
Karana-Ishvara, 132
Karl Lashley, 211
Karl Pribram, 210, 212
Karma-Gene Link, 8, 170
Karmic Cycle, 9, 238, 245
Karmic Footprints, 9, 225, 234, 238-239
Karmic Impression, 8, 169-170, 236-237, 240
Khala Jeevitarvava Tava, 21
Ki, 142

Kinetic Energy, 141, 150, 198, 221
Kirlian Photography, 136
Kundalini, 202-203, 246

L

Law of Action, 27
Law of Inertia, 27
Law of Karma, 153, 234-239
Laws of Matter, 54
Laxami, 110
Leaf, 134-135
Leonardo Da Vinci, 18
Lepton, 56, 89
Lepton Era, 89
Levels of Consciousness, 8, 188
Life After Life, 8, 150, 160, 230
Life Before Life, 8, 154
Life Cycle, 78, 152, 198
Light Cone, 77
Limbic System, 206-207
Logos, 111, 132
Lord Sri Krishna, 21
Louis de Broglie, 37, 39

M

Macrocosm, 7, 15, 69, 78, 93, 97, 113, 121, 141, 143, 160, 184
Magnetism, 27-29, 83, 143
Maha, 112, 241-242
Mahat, 107, 133
Mahavira, 19
Mandukya Upanishad, 197
Manhattan Project, 90
Mantra, 192, 201, 240-242, 245
Masaru Emoto, 176-177, 220
Mass Density, 92
Matrix, 7, 115-116

Max Born, 39-40
Max Muller, 155
Max Planck, 30-32
Memory Block, 154
Memory of Water, 8, 174, 176
Mental Paradox, 6, 42
Mexican Hat, 95
Michael Faraday, 28-29
Microcosm, 7, 15, 78, 113, 121, 123-124, 141, 143, 184, 203
Microtubules, 215-216
Midas Touch, 6, 43
Miller-Urey Experiment, 127, 129-130
Mind-Body, 132
Mind-Intellect, 9, 228
Mind-Thought Illusion, 8, 224
Mind-Thought-Consciousness, 8, 217
Mohenjodaro, 16
Moksha, 160
Molecule, 8, 38, 98, 129, 164-166, 168, 171-173, 175, 181, 210
Molecule of Life, 8, 164
Mysticism, 6, 61-62, 109, 201

N

Nadis, 8, 142, 199, 201, 218, 244
Nanocosm, 6, 14, 23-24, 41, 59, 93, 97, 184
Narada Purana, 18
Narmada, 203
NASA, 20, 114
Nature of Consciousness, 8, 187
Nature of Sound, 18
NDE, 150-151
Neuro-chemicals, 206
Neurohormonal, 200
Neurons, 62, 210, 212, 215-216

Quintillion, 213-214

R

Radioactivity, 55, 58
Radium, 82
Rajas, 59, 110, 134
Rajasic, 107, 132, 134
Reaction, 9, 14, 27, 63, 127, 129, 153, 156, 172-173, 207, 226, 236-237
Real Self, 195-196
Rebirth, 150-152, 160, 198-199
Reincarnation, 17, 151-152, 154-158, 160-161, 218, 237-238, 247
Relativity, 33, 73-75, 77, 83-86, 88, 93, 95, 120, 191
Replication, 171
Reproduction, 139, 167, 228-231
Resonance, 81, 191, 213
Respiration, 142
Ribonucleic Acid, 168
Richard Feynman, 95, 97
Rig Veda, 240, 242
Rishis, 17, 241
Robert M. Anderson, 191
Robert Wilson, 88, 91
Rosetta, 16, 36
Rosilyn Bruyere, 200

S

Sacral-Sexuality, 204
Sama Veda, 240, 242
Sambhoga-kaya, 109
Sat, 26, 30, 62, 79, 111, 118
Sat-Chit-Ananda, 105
Sattva, 59, 110, 134
Satya-Yuga, 113

Schema of Creation, 7, 132
Scott Hagan, 215
Sea of Light, 6, 59-60, 63, 105
Secrets of Reality, 3-5, 14, 21
Self Realized, 196
Self-Aware, 8, 105, 113, 118, 131, 180, 185
Self-Aware Universe, 8, 185, 246
Selfishness, 239-240
Selflessness, 239-240
Semyon Kirlian, 136
Senore Lucid Attarezde Salvio, 159
Serial Dilution, 175
Shakti, 202
Sheldon Glashow, 94, 97
Shiva, 60, 110, 112, 202-203
Short Wavelength, 29
Siddhartha Gautama, 111
Sigmund Freud, 188, 190
Sin, 236-237
Sindhu, 16
Sir John Woodroffe, 202
Sir Roger Penrose, 216
Sir William Bregg, 36
Sleep Cycle, 199
Sleep State, 137, 140, 189, 194-195
Socrates, 155
Space-Time, 7, 15, 60, 71-72, 76-77, 81, 84-85, 93, 96, 120, 153
Spatial Orientation, 7, 148
Speed of Light, 14, 46-47, 63, 72-75, 78, 81-82, 120, 140, 220-221, 245
Speed of Thought, 8, 15, 220
Sri Bharati Krsna Tirthaji, 20
Srngisodadhi Sandhiga, 21
St. Augustine, 81
St. Jerome, 155
Stanley Miller, 127, 130
States of Consciousness, 8, 193-195, 197, 227

Steven Weinberg, 97
Stress, 168-169, 203-204, 206-207, 221-223
String, 21, 94-97, 120, 164-165, 168
String Theory, 94-96, 120
Strong Force, 59, 94
Struck, 17-18, 127, 158, 180
Stuart Hameroff, 215-216
Subatomic, 6, 13-14, 18, 30, 34, 43, 47, 49, 53-57, 59-60, 63, 66-67, 70, 79, 91, 101, 130, 188, 216
Subatomic World, 6, 14, 30, 53-55, 66, 70, 130
Subconscious, 138, 189, 194, 198, 207
Sunlight, 77, 82, 98, 141, 218, 220, 231
Sunyata, 108
Superradiance, 215-216
Supraluminal, 140, 150-151, 161, 220-221, 245
Supreme Absolute, 1, 105, 154, 196
SUSY, 94-95
Swaha, 241-242
Syllabic, 78, 192, 201
Symmetry, 94-95
Sympathetic, 206-207
Synchronization, 192, 222-223, 245

T

T-cells, 205
T-lymphocytes, 205
Tamas, 59, 110, 134
Tamasic, 107, 132-134
Tan-mantras, 249
Temporal Reality, 117, 139-140
Terrestrial Life, 126

Raj Kapoor

Raj Kapoor is a physician, musician, philosopher, and a best-selling author. An international motivational speaker who has been featured on television and radio talk shows, his penetrating insight brings a fresh perspective to timeless topics. As an evocative writer, Kapoor makes complex ideas thoroughly understandable. He has explored the world of Reality and holistic thought through science and metaphysics uncovering the profound invisible power of human consciousness.

The former chair of the Department of Medicine, University of Pittsburgh Medical Center Passavant, Kapoor was appointed Professor of Yoga and Meditation, Hindu University of America, Florida, USA. He holds degrees and several honors and has devoted himself to the teaching of meditation, music and philosophies of life. He has more than two thousand hours of lectures, discourses and seminars on all aspects of philosophies worldwide.

Born in New Delhi, India, he currently resides with his wife in Pittsburgh, Pennsylvania USA.

12.16.2010

Correspondence

Requests for information on workshops and seminars by
Dr. Kapoor or any personal correspondence can be
addressed to:

Center for Wellness
9102 Babcock Blvd., Suite 101
Pittsburgh, PA: 15237

(412)-FOR-WELL
www.cfwbooks.com

Center for Wellness is unique in that it honors mental, physical and
spiritual well-being by taking into account the individual - genetics,
environmental factors, emotions, values and lifestyle habits - and
offers a personalized approach to healing the mind, body and soul.